DAVE RAMSEY'S

CORE

FINANCIAL WELLNESS

OUR MISSION:

*To empower and give HOPE to everyone from
the financially secure to the financially distressed.*

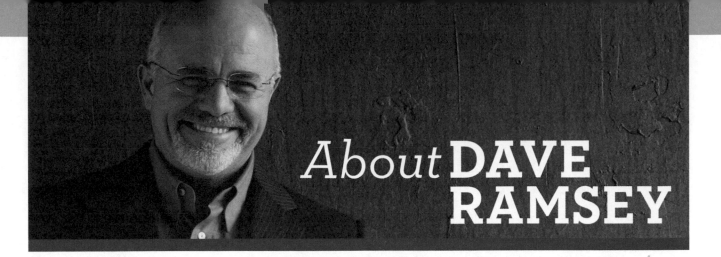

About DAVE RAMSEY

America's trusted voice on money and business, Dave Ramsey is a personal money-management expert and extremely popular national radio personality. His four *New York Times* best-selling books—*Financial Peace*, *More Than Enough*, *The Total Money Makeover* and *EntreLeadership*—have sold more than 7 million copies combined. *EntreLeadership: 20 Years of Practical Business Wisdom from the Trenches*, his latest best-seller, was released in September 2011 and debuted at number one.

By age 26 he had established a $4 million real estate portfolio, only to lose it by age 30. Using the wisdom he gained, Dave rebuilt his financial life and now teaches others how to be responsible with their money, so they can acquire enough wealth to take care of loved ones, retire with dignity, and give generously to others.

In 1992, he founded The Lampo Group, Inc. to provide financial counseling, through various means, to anyone who wants to better understand the principles of proper money management. Twenty years later, the company has grown from a card table in his living room to more than 300 team members and has been voted one of the best places to work in Nashville five times in a row. Dave runs a multi-million dollar company with a nationally recognized brand, but he defines success by the number of lives changed through his message of hope.

Dave offers that life-changing message as host of a nationally syndicated radio program, *The Dave Ramsey Show*, which is heard by 5 million listeners each week on more than 500 radio stations throughout the United States. In 2009, he was honored as the National Association of Broadcaster's Marconi Award winner.

He is the creator of *Financial Peace University* (FPU), a program that helps people dump their debt, get control of their money, and learn new behaviors around money that are founded on commitment and accountability. More than 1.5 million families have attended FPU classes at their workplace, church, military base, local nonprofit organization or community group.

Dave offers his message of hope through a variety of mediums and products. More than 900,000 people have attended a live event, including more than 40,000 EntreLeadership participants. His high school and college curriculums are offered in more than 10,000 schools and educational institutions. The "Dave Says" syndicated column is available to more than 17.5 million readers monthly. Thousands of children have enjoyed his entertaining and educational book series. Daveramsey.com offers free informational articles and live streaming of *The Dave Ramsey Show*.

He earned his B.S. in Finance and Real Estate from the University of Tennessee. Follow Dave on Twitter at @DaveRamsey and on the web at daveramsey.com.

HOW WELL ARE WE HANDLING MONEY?

The total American consumer debt is currently around

$2.5 TRILLION

THAT'S A 585% INCREASE IN THE LAST 30 YEARS!

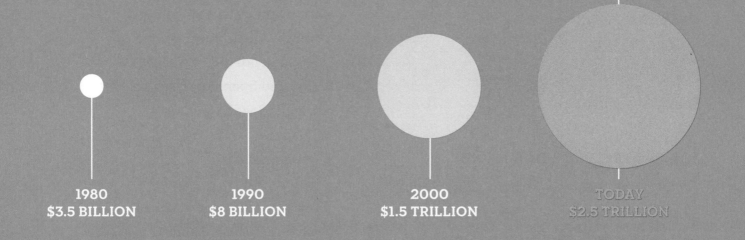

1980
$3.5 BILLION

1990
$8 BILLION

2000
$1.5 TRILLION

TODAY
$2.5 TRILLION

So, it's no wonder that a recent ComPsych study reported in USA Today found that a staggering

92% OF AMERICANS ARE LOSING SLEEP OVER THEIR FINANCES!

But what about retirement?

56% of American workers have less than $25,000 in retirement savings.

31% believe that they only need $250,000 or less in total retirement savings.

42% say they "guess" when asked how they make their retirement planning decisions.

28% spent more time watching reality TV last month than they spent planning and preparing for retirement over the past 10 years.

Depending on how your company chooses to offer CORE, you will most likely work through the program in one of two ways: a weekly workshop or an online self-study. Let's take a look at what you need to know about each class model.

WEEKLY WORKSHOP

The optional weekly workshop provides a lively group discussion format in addition to the great online tools. If your company offers the weekly workshop, you will watch each course's lesson videos outside of the office using CORE's powerful online learning system. There, you'll watch the videos, complete quizzes, and download additional tools and resources. Then, once a week, the group will get together for live discussions and some hands-on training activities to reinforce what you're learning online.

As you'll see throughout the program, personal finance is 80% behavior; it's only 20% head-knowledge. Working through this material with other men and women—participating as a group with a common goal—is the best way to really get at the behavior change needed to win with money.

ONLINE SELF-STUDY

If shift schedules, time conflicts or a scattered team prevent your organization from offering the weekly workshop, your company's leadership team may choose to offer the program as an online self-study. In this model, you'll have all the great online features available to those in the weekly workshop format, but you'll work through the entire program at your own pace without the optional live group discussions.

ONLINE RESOURCES

The goal of CORE is to give you access to this life-changing information on your schedule. Want to hear about budgeting on your lunch hour? Go for it. Want to watch with your spouse after you put the kids to bed? Grab some popcorn and make a date out of it! Want to learn the difference between a 401(k) and a 403(b) in your pajamas at 3:00 a.m.? Whatever works for you! With Dave Ramsey's CORE Financial Wellness, class is in session whenever you're ready!

Your CORE membership includes access to our cutting-edge online learning system. Whether you are participating in a weekly workshop or an online self-study, you will have several months access to these key online features:

- More that 14 hours of video teaching from Dave Ramsey, covering every major area of personal finance in beautiful streaming video that you can watch again and again!

- Exclusive downloadable resources, including full e-book versions of this workbook, printable budget forms and the full MP3 audio of every lesson!

- Lesson-by-lesson comments and discussions, allowing you to participate alongside your coworkers—and men and women in other companies taking the class all over the country!

- Powerful online budgeting software customized to Dave's popular zero-based budget and debt snowball strategies.

- "Ask Dave" topical search, giving you instant answers to your most common money questions and financial situations.

- Online quizzes at the end of every course to reinforce the principles and keep you heading in the right direction.

To get started, just complete the simple three-step registration at core.daveramsey.com using your company's unique enrollment key!

SECTION
101
THE POWER OF YOUR INCOME

superSAVING

PAYING YOURSELF FIRST

We're not a nation of savers. The typical American could not even cover a $5,000 emergency without having to borrow money. And big purchases? Nothing a swipe of the plastic can't take care of, right?

In *Super Saving*, Dave blasts through the hype and reveals the reasons why you should save money, how to be prepared for emergencies, and how to build genuine wealth—without luck or the lottery! More than that, Dave will truly get you excited about saving. Impossible? Not when you start *Super Saving*!

▶ **Video 1:** Save! Please, SAVE!

THE SEVEN BABY STEPS

There is a system for winning with money over time.
No matter where you are today, either financially
secure or financially distressed, these Baby Steps will
walk you step by step through the process.

STEP 1: $1,000 in an emergency fund
($500 if your income is under $20,000 per year)

STEP 2: Pay off all debt using the debt snowball
(does not include personal mortgage)

STEP 3: Three to six months of expenses in savings

STEP 4: Invest 15% of your household income into
Roth IRAs and pre-tax retirement plans

STEP 5: Save for your children's college education
using tax-favored plans

STEP 6: Pay off your home early

STEP 7: Build wealth and give!

$ _1000_ in the bank.

If your income is under $20,000, make this $ _4500_ .

Saving must become a _Priority_ .

You must pay yourself _First_ .

Give, save, then pay _Bill_ .

Saving money is about _Emotion_
and _Contentment_ .

Building wealth is not evil or wrong.
Money is _Amoral_ .

Larry Burkett, a famous Christian author, said,
"The only difference in saving and hoarding is
Attitude ."

▶ **Video 2:** Saving for Emergencies and Purchases

You should save for three basic reasons:

1. _Emergency_ _Fund_

2. _Purchases_

3. _Wealth_ _Building_

EMERGENCY FUND

___Unexpected___ events do occur—expect them!

Remember: Baby Step 1, a beginner emergency fund, is $___1,000___ in the bank (or $500 if your household income is below $20,000 per year).

BABY STEP ③

___3___ to ___6___ months of expenses in savings.

A great place to keep your emergency fund is in a ___Money___ ___Market___ account from a mutual fund company.

Your emergency fund is not an ___Investment___; it is ___Insurance___.

Do not ___Touch___ this fund for purchases!

The emergency fund is your ___First___ savings priority. Do it quickly!

KEY POINT

In our lives, we all go through "times of famine." Whether it's a layoff, lengthy illness, large financial loss, etc., we need to be prepared and save up while we can. It will allow us to better cope during tough times and, in some cases, to survive.

PURCHASES

Instead of __Borrowing__ to purchase, pay cash by using a __Sinking__ fund approach.

For example ...

Say you borrow to purchase a $ __4000__ dining room set. Most furniture stores will sell their financing contracts to finance companies.

This means you will have borrowed at __24__ % with payments of $ __201__ per month for __24__ months. So, you will pay a total of $ __5,064__, plus insurance, for that set.

But if you save the same $ __464__ per month for only __10__ months, you will be able to pay cash.

When you pay cash, you can almost always negotiate a discount, so you will be able to buy it even earlier.

Another example ...

Save for a $4,600 car by putting $ __464__ per month in the cookie jar for only 10 months!

Since we have pledged to borrow no more, this is the only way to make a purchase.

Daily decisions can make a HUGE impact!

EXPENSE	COST PER DAY	COST PER MONTH	IF INVESTED AT 12% FROM AGE 16-76
CIGARETTES	$3	$90	$11,622,000
GOURMET COFFEE	$5	$150	$19,371,943
LUNCH (5 DAYS/WEEK)	$8	$160	$20,663,319

IS IT WORTH THE COST IN THE LONG RUN?

▶ Video 3: Saving for Wealth Building

WEALTH BUILDING

RETIREMENT AND COLLEGE FUNDING

___Discipline___ is a key ingredient.

Building wealth is a ___Marathon___, not a ___Sprint___.

Just $ ___100___ per month, every month, from age 25 to age 65, at ___12___ % will build to over $ ___1,176,000___.

③ → ___Pre-Authorized___ ___Checking___ (PACs) withdrawals are a good way to build in discipline.

Compound interest is a mathematical ___explosion___.

You must start ___Now___ !

THE STORY OF BEN AND ARTHUR

Ben starts saving $2,000 a year ($167 a month) at age 19, stops saving at age 26, and never saves another dime. His brother, Arthur, starts later—at age 27—but saves until age 65, almost his entire life.

With a 12% rate of return, guess who comes out ahead at retirement?

WHAT DO WE LEARN FROM BEN AND ARTHUR?

- Rate of return, or _interest_ rate, is important.

- A simple, one-time investment of $1,000 could make a huge difference at retirement ... if you know how and where to invest it.

BEN vs. ARTHUR

BEN INVESTS	TOTAL	AGE	ARTHUR INVESTS	TOTAL
2,000	2,240	19	0	0
2,000	4,749	20	0	0
2,000	7,558	21	0	0
2,000	10,706	22	0	0
2,000	14,230	23	0	0
2,000	18,178	24	0	0
2,000	22,599	25	0	0
2,000	27,551	26	0	0
	30,857	27	2,000	2,240
	34,560	28	2,000	4,749
0	38,708	29	2,000	7,558
0	43,352	30	2,000	10,706
0	48,554	31	2,000	14,230
0	54,381	32	2,000	18,178
0	60,907	33	2,000	22,599
0	68,216	34	2,000	27,551
0	76,802	35	2,000	33,097
0	85,570	36	2,000	39,309
0	95,383	37	2,000	46,266
0	107,339	38	2,000	54,058
0	120,220	39	2,000	62,785
0	134,646	40	2,000	72,559
0	150,804	41	2,000	83,506
0	168,900	42	2,000	95,767
0	189,168	43	2,000	109,499
0	211,869	44	2,000	124,879
0	237,293	45	2,000	142,104
0	265,768	46	2,000	161,396
0	297,660	47	2,000	183,004
0	333,379	48	2,000	207,204
0	373,385	49	2,000	234,308
0	418,191	50	2,000	264,665
0	468,374	51	2,000	298,665
0	524,579	52	2,000	336,745
0	587,528	53	2,000	379,394
0	658,032	54	2,000	427,161
0	736,995	55	2,000	480,660
0	825,435	56	2,000	540,579
0	924,487	57	2,000	607,688
0	1,035,425	58	2,000	682,851
0	1,159,676	59	2,000	767,033
0	1,298,837	60	2,000	861,317
0	1,454,698	61	2,000	966,915
0	1,629,261	62	2,000	1,085,185
0	1,824,773	63	2,000	1,217,647
0	2,043,746	64	2,000	1,366,005
0	**2,288,996**	65	2,000	**1,532,166**

ARTHUR STARTS LATE

BEN STOPS SAVING!

$2,288,996 WITH ONLY A $16,000 INVESTMENT! **VS.** **$1,532,166** ARTHUR NEVER CAUGHT UP!

THE BASIC QUICKIE BUDGET

This form will help you get your feet wet in the area of budgeting. It is only one page and should not be intimidating as you get started. The purpose of this form is to show you exactly how much money you need every month in order to survive. We won't get into the details of your credit card bills, student loans and other consumer debts here. This is just to give you a starting point as you begin to take control of your money.

There are four columns on this form:

1 *Monthly Total*
- This column shows you how much you are spending on necessities each month.
- If you do not know the amount, write down your best estimate.
- If an estimate is grossly inaccurate, then you may have never even noticed how much you were spending in that area before now. Don't beat yourself up about this!

2 *Payoff Total*
- Write down how much money is required to completely pay off that item.
- This line only appears in the relevant categories (mortgage, car debt, etc.).

3 *How Far Behind?*
- If your account is past due in any category, write down how many days you are behind.
- If you are up-to-date, simply write a zero or "N/A" (not applicable) in this column.

4 *Type of Account*
- Write in how this area is paid—by check, automatic bank draft, cash, etc.
- Early in the program, you will see the benefits of using cash for certain items. Challenge yourself by identifying categories for which you can use cash only.
- The asterisks (*) on the form indicate areas in which a cash-based approach could be helpful.

THE BASIC QUICKIE BUDGET

Item	1 Monthly Total	2 Payoff Total	3 How Far Behind	4 Type of Account
GIVING	$366		NA	Check
SAVING	$100		NA	Bank Draft
HOUSING				
First Mortgage	$915	$125,000	NA	Bank Draft
Second Mortgage	____	____	____	____
Repairs/Mn. Fee	____		____	____
UTILITIES				
Electricity	$100		NA	Check
Water	$55		NA	Check
Gas	$75		NA	Check
Phone	$45		NA	Check
Trash	____		____	____
Cable	$21		NA	Check
*Food	$360		NA	Cash
TRANSPORTATION				
Car Payment	$400	$8,500	2 months	Check
Car Payment	____	____	____	____
*Gas & Oil	$200		NA	Cash
*Repairs & Tires	____		____	____
Car Insurance	$80		NA	Check
*CLOTHING	$100		NA	Cash
PERSONAL				
Disability Ins.	____		____	____
Health Insurance	$300		NA	Bank Draft
Life Insurance	____		____	____
Child Care	____		____	____
*Entertainment	$200		NA	Cash
OTHER MISC.	____		____	____

TOTAL MONTHLY NECESSITIES $3,317

Go online to take your quiz for *Super Saving*!

BABY STEPS

Here's a review of the Baby Steps covered in this lesson:

 $1,000 in the bank
For more insight, see Chapter 6 of *The Total Money Makeover*.

 3-6 months of expenses in savings
For more insight, see Chapter 8 of *The Total Money Makeover*.

ANSWER KEY

1,000	First
500	Borrowing
Priority	Sinking
First	4,000
Bills	24
Emotion	211
Contentment	24
Amoral	5,064
Attitude	211
Emergency	18
Fund	464
Purchases	Discipline
Wealth	Marathon
Building	Sprint
Unexpected	100
1,000	12
3	1,176,000
6	Pre-Authorized
Money	Checking
Market	Explosion
Investment	Now
Insurance	Interest
Touch	

KEY POINTS

1. Savings must become a priority.

2. You should save for an emergency fund, major purchases and wealth building.

3. Decide and agree with your spouse on what qualifies as an emergency for your family.

QUESTIONS FOR REFLECTION

1. What is Baby Step 1? Why is this important?

   $1000 in the Emergency Fund. / Process of Starting to Save

2. Why do you think so many people use debt (credit cards, loans, etc.) for emergencies?

   Easy to Use and No Waiting

3. Dave used the analogy of the brick to show that money is amoral. What did this illustration mean to you?

   Helped Show Me That we need to learn to Mold our Money to Work For Us

4. How does the idea of an emergency fund change the way you view "emergencies"?

   Need To Help Me Identify What is an emergency

5. What would constitute a financial emergency in your situation? How would you handle that today?

   Medical / Appliance Breaking / Vehicle Broke / Home Emergency   Today Do Our Best To Pay Cash Rest on Credit Cards.

6. Think about how much money you would need to cover 3-6 months of expenses. How would having that emergency fund in the bank change your day-to-day life? What do you think prevents most people from saving an emergency fund?

   Having The Emergency fund of 3-6 months can cover All Emergency But Need To Pay Yourself Back First.

PERSONAL APPLICATION

After viewing *Super Saving*, be sure to complete these action items before moving on to the next lesson.

- Complete the Quickie Budget form in the back of this workbook or in the online resources.

- Start watching the credit card offers that come in the mail. Open them up, make a note of the amount of credit they're offering, and then shred them! Keep a running tally of how much debt you are offered—and avoided—as you work through the class.

- Optional: Read Chapters 1, 2, 6 and 8 of *The Total Money Makeover*.

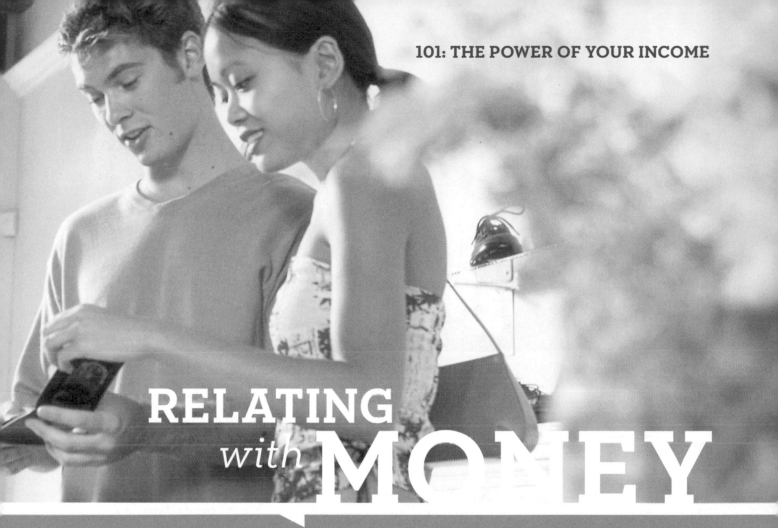

RELATING *with* MONEY

COUPLES, SINGLES AND KIDS

How we handle our money impacts every part of our lives. It is a huge factor in marriage, a tremendous responsibility in parenting, and a potential landmine for singles.

In *Relationships And Money*, Dave shows couples how to work together as a team, gives singles some practical tips for financial accountability, and helps parents teach their children about money from a young age. You'll discover that money is rarely *just* about money. Usually, it is about so much more!

RELATIONSHIPS
with MONEY

▶ Video 1: Marriage and Money

MEN, WOMEN AND MONEY
OVERGENERALIZING

The flow of money in a family represents the __Value System__ under which that family operates.

EMERGENCY FUND SAVINGS
Men: "It's boring and not __Sophisticated__ enough."

Women: "It's the most __Important__ key to our financial plan."

SHOPPING
Men get good deals by __Negotiating__.

Men want to win.

Women get good deals by __Hunting__.

Women enjoy the process.

FINANCIAL PROBLEMS

Men lose _Self_ - _Esteem_ because money usually represents a _Score card_ to them.

Women face _fear_ or even _terror_ because, with women, money usually represents _Security_.

MARRIAGE AND MONEY

CAN WE TALK?

The number-one cause of divorce in America is _Money_ _fights_.

When you agree on your value system, you will reach a _Unity_ in your marriage that you can experience no other way.

▶ **Video 2:** Nerds, Free Spirits and Singles

WHO DOES THE FINANCIAL DECISION-MAKING?

Both of you!

The partner with the natural _Gift_ can prepare the _Budget_, but the decision-making must be done by _Both_.

The _Nerd_ likes doing the budget because it gives them control, and they feel like they are taking care of loved ones.

The _Free_ _Spirit_ feels controlled, not cared for, and can appear irresponsible to the nerd.

"Therefore a man shall leave his father and mother and be joined to his wife, and they shall become one flesh."

—Old Testament

"No man is wise enough by himself."

—Titus Maccius Plautus

"It is unwise to be too sure of one's own wisdom. It is healthy to be reminded that the strongest might weaken and the wisest might err."

—Mahatma Gandhi

SINGLES AND MONEY

Time _Poverty_ and fatigue can lead to poor money management.

Beware of _Impulse_ buying, which can be brought on by _Stress_ or even by the "I owe it to _Myself_" syndrome.

A written plan gives the single person _Empowerment_, self-accountability and _Control_.

KEY POINT

Accountability and support are the ladders that lift us up from life's pits.

PREVENTION

Develop an _Accountability_ relationship.

This is someone with whom to discuss major _Purchases_ and your _Budget_.

Accountability friends must love you enough to be brutally honest and promise to do so for your own good.

▶ **Video 3:** Kids and Money

KIDS AND MONEY

Teaching your kids how to handle money is not the _Schools_ responsibility. It is _Your_ responsibility!

Pay ___Commissions___, not allowance;
we have enough people in our society who expect to
be made allowance for.

Words are ___Powerful___.

If you ___Work___, you get paid; if you do not
___Work___, you do not get paid.

Teach by ___Example___.

Show them how you live ___Debt___ free,
how insurance works, how an IRA works, etc.

BE AGE-APPROPRIATE

If the children are young, use a clear ___Container___
to save. Visual reinforcement is powerful.

Use three envelopes for ages 5–12:
___Giving___, ___Spending___ and ___Saving___.

Somewhere around 13–15 years old, open a
___Checking___ ___Account___ for
the child and teach him/her how to run it by
monthly reviews.

NEXT STEPS

Something get your attention in this lesson? Write it down!

Saving Up and Paying Cash is like Paying Yourself
Better To Put a Plan Together

KEY POINTS

1. Men and women approach money very differently.

2. Every relationship has a Nerd and a Free Spirit.

3. Singles need to find an accountability partner to discuss finances and purchases with.

4. Parents should use age-appropriate techniques to teach their children how to handle money.

QUESTIONS FOR REFLECTION

1. What are the advantages to being single in regards to financial control? What are the disadvantages?

   Advantages are Getting To Do What You Want and How You Want to Spend It.
   Disadvantages — No One to Help keep You In Check

2. What are some of the reasons that finances should be agreed upon by both partners in a marriage?

   To Help Challenge Each Other For Priorities On What To Pay

3. How do you prioritize your time and resources during periods of financial stress? What impact—either positive or negative—has this had on your relationships?

Positive - We Both know We need to Get Back
On Track

4. What are some practical ways to teach your children about money?

To let Them See What Mistakes We Have
Made.

5. Respond to this statement: "How you spend your money tells me who you are and what is important to you."

This is to important in today the way
people think. They Believe you must Spend
It to Show Something For It.

PERSONAL APPLICATION

After viewing *Relationships and Money*, be sure to complete these action items before moving on to the next lesson.

- If you're married, schedule time with your spouse this week to have your first Budget Committee Meeting. Make this an initial "State of the Union" discussion, taking an honest look at where you are financially as well as where you'd like to be someday.

- If you're single, identify an appropriate accountability partner using the guidelines Dave outlined in this lesson.

CASH flow PLANNING

THE NUTS AND BOLTS OF BUDGETING

Oh no! The dreaded "B" word: budget! Many people are scared to death of the very idea of a budget. It drums up images of living on bread and water and a dull, dreary, no-frills way of life. That's not what we're talking about!

The truth is, the budget is your key to success! Like Dave says, money makes a fantastic servant, but it is a horrible master. And if you don't tell your money where to go and what to do, it will definitely master you the rest of your life. In *Cash Flow Planning*, you'll learn how to make your money work for you and how to put together a household budget that really works!

CASH flow PLANNING

▶ **Video 1:** The Truth About Budgeting

WISDOM

"Be diligent to know the state of your flocks, and attend to your herds."

—Old Testament

BUDGETING BASICS

Money is ___Active___.

You must do a written ___Cash___ ___Flow___ plan every month.

You must also keep your checking account ___Balanced___.

Overdrafts are a sign of ___Crisis___ ___Living___ and sloppy, lazy money habits.

Use ___Duplicates___ checks if necessary.

If not managed and made to behave, the ___Atm___ card and the ___Debit___ card are certain to become budget busters.

REASONS WE DON'T DO A CASH FLOW PLAN

Most people hate the word "budget" for four reasons:

1. It has a ___Straightjacket___ connotation.

2. It has been used to ___abuse___ them.

3. They've never had a budget that ___Worked___.

4. Paralysis from ___fear___ of what they will find.

Cash flow plans do not work when you:

1. ___Leave___ things ___Out___.

2. ___Overcomplicate___ your plan.

3. Don't actually ___Do___ it.

4. Don't actually ___Live___ on it.

▶ **Video 2:** Why Bother?

REASONS WE SHOULD DO A CASH FLOW PLAN

A written plan removes the "management by ___Crisis___" from your finances.

Managed money goes ___Farther___.

A written plan, if actually lived and agreed on, will remove many of the ___Money___ ___Fight___ from your marriage.

WISDOM

"People don't plan to fail, they fail to plan."

—Anonymous

"To accomplish great things, we must dream as well as act."

—Anatole France

Food
Shelter
Transportation
Utilities

KEY POINT

Budgeting is not a method by which you make other people behave. Budgeting is a method by which you make *money* behave.

Most adults are pretty good at budgeting—when they bother to do it on purpose. Some basics include:

- Keeping up with your receipts and writing them in your account register.

- Using your bank's online tools to keep a close eye on your spending.

Remember the Four Walls

No matter how tight your budget gets, never lose sight of these four priorities:

1. FOOD
2. SHELTER
3. CLOTHING
4. TRANSPORTATION

A written plan, if actually lived and agreed on, will remove much of the _____Guilt_____, _____Shame_____ and _____Fear_____ that may now be a part of buying necessities such as food or clothing.

A written plan, if actually lived and agreed on, will remove many of the _____Overdrafts_____ from your life, consequently removing a lot of _____Stress_____.

A written plan, if actually lived and agreed on, will show if you are _____Overspending_____ in a certain area.

The easiest and most powerful method is a _Zero_-based plan using the _____Envelope_____ system.

▶ Video 3: Building a Better Budget

FINANCIAL MANAGEMENT FORMS

Welcome to the wonderful world of cash flow management! By filling out just a few forms, your new financial plan will start to unfold right in front of you. You'll immediately identify problem areas and learn how to close the valve of wasteful spending, because you'll know exactly where all of your dollars are going!

It will probably take a little while to complete the forms the first time. After that initial startup, however, you'll get better and better until budgeting becomes second nature.

Complete the whole set of forms to get started. Then, you'll only need to do the Monthly Cash Flow Plan (Form 5), Allocated Spending Plan (Form 7) or the Irregular Income Plan (Form 8) once a month. Dave will teach you which form best fits your specific situation. This should only take about 30 minutes a month once you get in the habit.

You'll also want to update the whole set of forms once a year or whenever you experience a dramatic positive or negative financial event (such as receiving a large inheritance or paying for a major house repair).

Use the examples on the following pages as a guide. You can download all the forms in a printable PDF format from the website, and you can even use the online budgeting tool as a replacement for the Monthly Cash Flow Plan (Form 5).

Are you ready? It's time to make those dollars dance! Go for it!

	Action Needed	Action Date
Written Cash Flow Plan	Complete first budget	NOW!
Will and/or Estate Plan	Make an appt. with lawyer	June 6
Debt Reduction Plan	Begin debt snowball	July 1
Tax Reduction Plan	NA	NA
Emergency Funding	On hold until Baby Step 3	NA
Retirement Funding	On hold until Baby Step 4	NA
College Funding	On hold until Baby Step 5	NA
Charitable Giving	Start tithing	June 15
Teach My Children	Get Financial Peace Jr.	August
Life Insurance	Done	NA
Health Insurance	Done	NA
Disability Insurance	Check company options	This week
Auto Insurance	Check current policy details	July 1
Homeowner's Insurance	Check replacement cost	This week

I (We) __Joe & Suzie Public__, (a) responsible adult(s), do hereby promise to take the above stated actions by the above stated dates to financially secure the well-being of my (our) family and myself (ourselves).

Signed: __Joe Q. Public__ Date: __June 2__

Signed: __Suzie Q. Public__ Date: __June 2__

Item/Describe	Value	–	Debt	=	Equity
Real Estate _____	$180,000		$149,000		$31,000
Real Estate _____					
Car _____	$2,500				$2,500
Car _____	$3,000				$3,000
Cash On Hand					
Checking Account					
Checking Account					
Savings Account	$1,600				$1,600
Money Market Account					
Mutual Funds					
Retirement Plan 1	$400				$400
Retirement Plan 2	$8,000				$8,000
Cash Value (Insurance)					
Household Items	$30,000				$30,000
Jewelry					
Antiques					
Boat					
Unsecured Debt (Negative)					
Credit Card Debt (Negative)					
Other _____					
Other _____					
Other _____					
TOTAL	$225,500		$149,000		$76,500

Source	Amount	Period/Describe
Salary 1	$2,716	1st of Month
Salary 2	$945	1st & 15th – $472⁵⁰
Salary 3		
Bonus		
Self-Employment		
Interest Income		
Dividend Income		
Royalty Income		
Rents		
Notes		
Alimony		
Child Support		
AFDC		
Unemployment		
Social Security		
Pension		
Annuity		
Disability Income		
Cash Gifts		
Trust Fund		
Other_____		
Other_____		
Other_____		
TOTAL	$3,661	

04 LUMP SUM PAYMENT PLANNING

Payments you make on a non-monthly basis, such as insurance premiums and taxes, can be budget busters if you do not plan for them every month. Therefore, you must annualize the cost and convert these to monthly budget items. That way, you can save the money each month and will not be caught off-guard when your bi-monthly, quarterly, semi-annual or annual bills come due. Simply divide the annual cost by 12 to determine the monthly amount you should save for each item.

Item Needed	Annual Amount		Monthly Amount
Real Estate Taxes	_____	/ 12 =	_____
Homeowner's Insurance	_____	/ 12 =	_____
Home Repairs	_____	/ 12 =	_____
Replace Furniture	_____	/ 12 =	_____
Medical Bills	_____	/ 12 =	_____
Health Insurance	_____	/ 12 =	_____
Life Insurance	_____	/ 12 =	_____
Disability Insurance	_____	/ 12 =	_____
Car Insurance	_____	/ 12 =	_____
Car Repair/Tags	_____	/ 12 =	_____
Replace Car	_____	/ 12 =	_____
Clothing	_____	/ 12 =	_____
Tuition	_____	/ 12 =	_____
Bank Note	_____	/ 12 =	_____
IRS (Self-Employed)	_____	/ 12 =	_____
Vacation	_____	/ 12 =	_____
Gifts (including Christmas)	$1,200	/ 12 =	$100
Other: _____	_____	/ 12 =	_____

MONTHLY CASH FLOW PLAN

Every single dollar of your income should be allocated to some category on this form. When you're done, your total income minus expenses should equal zero. If it doesn't, then you need to adjust some categories (such as debt reduction, giving or saving) so that it does equal zero. Use some common sense here too. Do not leave things like clothes, car repairs or home improvements off this list. If you don't plan for these things, you're only setting yourself up for failure later.

Yes, this budget form is long. It's really long. We do that so that we can list practically every expense imaginable on this form to prevent you from forgetting something. Don't expect to put something on every line item. Just use the ones that are relevant to your specific situation.

Every main category on this form has subcategories. Fill in the monthly expense for each subcategory, and then write down the grand total for that category. Later, as you actually pay the bills and work through the month, use the "Actually Spent" column to record what you really spent in each area. If there is a substantial difference between what you budgeted and what you spent, then you'll need to readjust the budget to make up for the difference. If one category continually comes up over or short for two or three months, you'll need to adjust the budgeted amount accordingly.

Notes:
- An asterisk (*) beside an item indicates an area for which you should use a cash envelope system.

- The emergency fund should get all the savings until you've completed your full emergency fund of three to six months of expenses (Baby Step 3).

- Don't forget to include your annualized items from the Lump Sum Payment Planning sheet (Form 4), including your Christmas gift planning.

Budgeted Item	Sub Total	TOTAL	Actually Spent	% of Take Home Pay
CHARITABLE GIFTS		$366	_____	10%
SAVING				
Emergency Fund	$224		_____	
Retirement Fund	_____		_____	
College Fund	_____	$224	_____	6%
HOUSING				
First Mortgage	$915		_____	
Second Mortgage	_____		_____	
Real Estate Taxes	_____		_____	
Homeowner's Ins.	_____		_____	
Repairs or Mn. Fee	_____		_____	
Replace Furniture	$50		_____	
Other _____	_____	$965	_____	27%
UTILITIES				
Electricity	$100		_____	
Water	$55		_____	
Gas	$75		_____	
Phone	$45		_____	
Trash	_____		_____	
Cable	$21	$296	_____	8%
*FOOD				
*Grocery	$360		_____	
*Restaurants	$50	$410	_____	12%
TRANSPORTATION				
Car Payment	_____		_____	
Car Payment	_____		_____	
*Gas and Oil	$150		_____	
*Repairs and Tires	_____		_____	
Car Insurance	$80		_____	
License and Taxes	_____		_____	
Car Replacement	_____	$230	_____	5%
PAGE 1 TOTAL		$2,491	_____	

Budgeted Item	Sub Total	TOTAL	Actually Spent	% of Take Home Pay
*CLOTHING				
*Children	$100			
*Adults	___		___	
*Cleaning/Laundry	___	$100	___	3%
MEDICAL/HEALTH				
Disability Insurance	$300		___	
Health Insurance	$50		___	
Doctor Bills	$20		___	
Dentist	___		___	
Optometrist	___		___	
Medications	___	$370	___	10%
PERSONAL				
Life Insurance	$65		___	
Child Care	___		___	
*Baby Sitter	___		___	
*Toiletries	___		___	
*Cosmetics	___		___	
*Hair Care	$60		___	
Education/Adult	___		___	
School Tuition	___		___	
School Supplies	___		___	
Child Support	___		___	
Alimony	___		___	
Subscriptions	___		___	
Organization Dues	$25		___	
Gifts (incl. Christmas)	___		___	
Miscellaneous	$50		___	
*Blow Money	$100	$300	___	8%
PAGE 2 TOTAL		$770		

05 | MONTHLY CASH FLOW PLAN (CONTINUED)

Budgeted Item	Sub Total	TOTAL	Actually Spent	% of Take Home Pay
RECREATION				
*Entertainment	$50			
Vacation	$25	$75		2%
DEBTS (Hopefully $0!)				
Visa 1	$100			
Visa 2				
Master Card 1	$75			
Master Card 2				
American Express	$50			
Discover Card				
Gas Card 1				
Gas Card 2				
Dept. Store Card 1				
Dept. Store Card 2				
Finance Co. 1				
Finance Co. 2				
Credit Line				
Student Loan 1	$100			
Student Loan 2				
Other _____				
Other _____				
Other _____				
Other _____		$325		9%
PAGE 3 TOTAL		$400		
PAGE 2 TOTAL		$770		
PAGE 1 TOTAL		$2,491		
GRAND TOTAL		$3661		
TOTAL HOUSEHOLD INCOME		$3661		
		ZERO		

06 RECOMMENDED PERCENTAGES

How much of your income should be spent on housing, giving, food, etc.? Through experience and research, we recommend the following percentages. However, you should remember that these are only *recommended* percentages. If you have an unusually high or low income, then these numbers could change dramatically. For example, if you have a high income, the percentage spent on food will be much lower than someone with a low income.

If you find that you spend much more in one category than we recommend, however, it may be necessary to adjust your lifestyle in that area in order to enjoy more freedom and flexibility across the board.

Item	Actual %	Recommended %
CHARITABLE GIFTS	10%	10–15%
SAVING	6%	5–10%
HOUSING	27%	25–35%
UTILITIES	8%	5–10%
FOOD	12%	5–15%
TRANSPORTATION	5%	10–15%
CLOTHING	3%	2–7%
MEDICAL/HEALTH	10%	5–10%
PERSONAL	8%	5–10%
RECREATION	2%	5–10%
DEBTS	9%	5–10%

ALLOCATED SPENDING PLAN

This form goes into deeper detail than the Monthly Cash Flow Plan (Form 5). Here, you will allocate—or spend—all of your money from each individual pay period.

There are four columns on this form, representing the four weeks in a given month. You will use one column for each week you get paid. If you are married and your spouse earns an income, you will both use this same form. For weeks in which you both receive a paycheck, add those two incomes together and use a single column.

Now, go down the list and allocate each expense to a specific payday, using your bills' due dates as a guide. For example, if your phone bill is due on the 22nd and you get paid on the 15th and 30th, then you know that you would probably pay that bill from your income on the 15th. The point is to anticipate your upcoming expenses and income and plan accordingly.

Beside each line item, you'll see two blanks separated by a slash (/). Put the expense to the left of the slash and the remaining income from that pay period to the right of the slash. As you work your way down the column, the income remaining should diminish until you reach a perfect zero at the bottom of the list. If you have money left over at the end of the column, go back and adjust an area, such as savings or giving, so that you spend every single dollar.

NOTES:
1. If you have an irregular income, such as self-employment or commissions, you should use the Irregular Income Planning sheet (Form 8) instead of the Allocated Spending Plan (Form 7).

2. If you know that you have an impulse spending problem, you may want to allocate more money to the "Blow" category. That way, you are at least setting up some spending boundaries.

3. An asterisk (*) beside an item indicates an area for which you should use a cash envelope system.

PAY PERIOD:	7 / 1	7 / 8	7 / 15	7 / 22

ITEM:

INCOME	$3,188	0	$472	0

CHARITABLE	366 / 2822	___ / ___	___ / ___	___ / ___

SAVING

Emergency Fund	224 / 2598	___ / ___	___ / ___	___ / ___
Retirement Fund	___ / ___	___ / ___	___ / ___	___ / ___
College Fund	___ / ___	___ / ___	___ / ___	___ / ___

HOUSING

First Mortgage	915 / 1683	___ / ___	___ / ___	___ / ___
Second Mortgage	___ / ___	___ / ___	___ / ___	___ / ___
Real Estate Taxes	___ / ___	___ / ___	___ / ___	___ / ___
Homeowner's Ins.	___ / ___	___ / ___	___ / ___	___ / ___
Repairs or Mn. Fees	___ / ___	___ / ___	___ / ___	___ / ___
Replace Furniture	___ / ___	___ / ___	___ / ___	___ / ___
Other: _____	___ / ___	___ / ___	50 / 422	___ / ___

UTILITIES

Electricity	100 / 1583	___ / ___	___ / ___	___ / ___
Water	___ / ___	___ / ___	55 / 367	___ / ___
Gas	___ / ___	___ / ___	75 / 292	___ / ___
Phone	45 / 1538	___ / ___	___ / ___	___ / ___
Trash	___ / ___	___ / ___	___ / ___	___ / ___
Cable	21 / 1517	___ / ___	___ / ___	___ / ___

*FOOD

*Grocery	200 / 1317	___ / ___	160 / 132	___ / ___
*Restaurants	25 / 1292	___ / ___	25 / 107	___ / ___

TRANSPORTATION

Car Payment	____ / ____	____ / ____	____ / ____	____ / ____
Car Payment	____ / ____	____ / ____	____ / ____	____ / ____
* Gas and Oil	75 / 1217	____ / ____	75 / 32	____ / ____
* Repairs and Tires	____ / ____	____ / ____	____ / ____	____ / ____
Car Insurance	80 / 1137	____ / ____	____ / ____	____ / ____
License and Taxes	____ / ____	____ / ____	____ / ____	____ / ____
Car Replacement	____ / ____	____ / ____	____ / ____	____ / ____

*CLOTHING

* Children	____ / ____	____ / ____	____ / ____	____ / ____
* Adults	100 / 1037	____ / ____	____ / ____	____ / ____
* Cleaning/Laundry	____ / ____	____ / ____	____ / ____	____ / ____

MEDICAL/HEALTH

Disability Insurance	____ / ____	____ / ____	____ / ____	____ / ____
Health Insurance	300 / 131	____ / ____	____ / ____	____ / ____
Doctor	50 / 681	____ / ____	____ / ____	____ / ____
Dentist	____ / ____	____ / ____	20 / 12	____ / ____
Optometrist	____ / ____	____ / ____	____ / ____	____ / ____
Medications	____ / ____	____ / ____	____ / ____	____ / ____

PERSONAL

Life Insurance	65 / 622	____ / ____	____ / ____	____ / ____
Child Care	____ / ____	____ / ____	____ / ____	____ / ____
* Baby Sitter	____ / ____	____ / ____	____ / ____	____ / ____
* Toiletries	____ / ____	____ / ____	____ / ____	____ / ____
* Cosmetics	____ / ____	____ / ____	____ / ____	____ / ____
* Hair Care	____ / ____	____ / ____	____ / ____	____ / ____
Education/Adult	60 / 562	____ / ____	____ / ____	____ / ____
School Tuition	____ / ____	____ / ____	____ / ____	____ / ____
School Supplies	____ / ____	____ / ____	____ / ____	____ / ____
Child Support	____ / ____	____ / ____	____ / ____	____ / ____

Alimony	___ / ___	___ / ___	___ / ___	___ / ___
Subscriptions	___ / ___	___ / ___	___ / ___	___ / ___
Organization Dues	25 / 537	___ / ___	___ / ___	___ / ___
Gifts (incl. Christmas)	___ / ___	___ / ___	___ / ___	___ / ___
Miscellaneous	50 / 487	___ / ___	___ / ___	___ / ___
*BLOW $$	100 / 387	___ / ___	___ / ___	___ / ___
RECREATION				
* Entertainment	50 / 331	___ / ___	___ / ___	___ / ___
Vacation	25 / 312	___ / ___	___ / ___	___ / ___
DEBTS (Hopefully $0!)				
Visa 1	100 / 212	___ / ___	___ / ___	___ / ___
Visa 2	___ / ___	___ / ___	___ / ___	___ / ___
MasterCard 1	75 / 137	___ / ___	___ / ___	___ / ___
MasterCard 2	___ / ___	___ / ___	___ / ___	___ / ___
American Express	50 / 87	___ / ___	___ / ___	___ / ___
Discover Card	___ / ___	___ / ___	___ / ___	___ / ___
Gas Card 1	___ / ___	___ / ___	___ / ___	___ / ___
Gas Card 2	___ / ___	___ / ___	___ / ___	___ / ___
Dept. Store Card 1	___ / ___	___ / ___	___ / ___	___ / ___
Dept. Store Card 2	___ / ___	___ / ___	___ / ___	___ / ___
Finance Co. 1	___ / ___	___ / ___	___ / ___	___ / ___
Finance Co. 2	___ / ___	___ / ___	___ / ___	___ / ___
Credit Line	___ / ___	___ / ___	___ / ___	___ / ___
Student Loan 1	___ / ___	___ / ___	___ / ___	___ / ___
Student Loan 2	___ / ___	___ / ___	___ / ___	___ / ___
Other _____	___ / ___	___ / ___	___ / ___	___ / ___
Other _____	87 / 0	___ / ___	12 / 0	___ / ___

Many people have an "irregular" income, which simply means that their compensation fluctuates from month to month. This is especially common for the self-employed, as well as commission-based salespeople. While this makes it more difficult to predict your income, you are still responsible for doing a monthly budget!

The Monthly Cash Flow Plan (Form 5) should remain a crucial part of your plan, as it lays out exactly how much money you need to bring home each month to survive and prosper. However, instead of doing the Allocated Spending Plan (Form 7), you will use this Irregular Income Planning sheet.

On this form, simply look at the individual items from your Monthly Cash Flow Plan sheet and prioritize them by importance. Ask yourself, "If I only have enough money to pay one thing, what would that be?" Put that at the top of your list. Then, ask yourself, "If I only have enough money to pay one more thing, what would that be?" That's number two. Keep this up all the way down the list.

With your list in place, you're ready to get paid. If you get a $1,500 paycheck, you will spend that $1,500 right down the list until it is gone, recording the cumulative amount spent in the "Cumulative Amount" column. At that point, you're finished spending, no matter what remains unpaid on the list. That's why the most important things are at the top of the list, right?

Be prepared to stand your ground. Things usually have a way of seeming important when they are only urgent. For example, a once-in-a-lifetime opportunity to see your favorite band perform live may seem important, but in reality, it is only urgent, meaning that it is time-sensitive. Urgency alone should not move an item to the top of this list!

Item	Amount	Cumulative Amount
JC Penney	$150	$150
Sears	$250	$400
Visa	$500	$900
Vacation – part	$200	$1100
Christmas	$400	$1500

BREAKDOWN OF SAVINGS

After you have fully funded your emergency fund, you can start to save for other items, such as furniture, car replacement, home maintenance or a vacation. This sheet will remind you that every dollar in your savings account is already committed to something. For example, it's a bad idea to take money away from car repairs to pay for an impulse Hawaiian vacation, even if you pay cash for it. What would you do if the car broke down the week you got back home? However, it can be okay to re-assign the dollars to another category, as long as you do it on purpose and it doesn't put you in a pinch in another category. Keep up with your breakdown of savings every month, one quarter at a time.

Item		Balance By Month		
		October	November	December
Emergency Fund (1)	$1,000	_____	_____	_____
Emergency Fund (2)	3-6 months	_____	_____	_____
Retirement Fund		_____	_____	_____
College Fund		_____	_____	_____
Real Estate Taxes		_____	_____	_____
Homeowner's Insurance		_____	_____	_____
Repairs or Mn. Fee		_____	_____	_____
Replace Furniture		_____	_____	_____
Car Insurance		_____	_____	_____
Car Replacement		$600	$700	$800
Disability Insurance		_____	_____	_____
Health Insurance		$500	$500	$500
Doctor		_____	_____	_____
Dentist		_____	_____	_____
Optometrist		_____	_____	_____
Life Insurance		_____	_____	_____
School Tuition		_____	_____	_____
School Supplies		_____	_____	_____
Gifts (incl. Christmas)		$500	$650	$800
Vacation		_____	_____	_____
Other _____		_____	_____	_____
Other _____		_____	_____	_____
TOTAL		$1,600	$1,850	$2,100

Go online to take your quiz for *Cash Flow Planning*!

NEXT STEPS

Something get your attention in this lesson? Write it down!

ANSWER KEY

Active	Do
Cash Flow	Live
Balanced	Crisis
Crisis Living	Farther
Duplicate	Money Fights
ATM	Guilt
Debit	Shame
Straitjacket	Fear
Abuse	Overdrafts
Worked	Stress
Fear	Overspending
Leave	Zero
Out	Envelope
Overcomplicate	

KEY POINTS

1. Spend every dollar on paper, on purpose, before the month begins.

2. Try the envelope system for the next three months.

3. Give your budget 90 days to really start working.

QUESTIONS FOR REFLECTION

1. What are the benefits of a written cash flow plan?

   To Control Your Money

2. How can a written budget impact a marriage or empower a single person?

   Will Need To Bring Out Everything

3. Does budgeting come naturally to you? Would you consider yourself a Nerd or a Free Spirit?

   No It Does Not
   Mix Of The Two But FreeSpirit

4. How can the Four Walls (food, shelter, clothing, transportation) help you prioritize your spending?

Keep Your Priorities in Check

5. What is your reaction to the concept of a cash envelope system? What are the pros and cons in your opinion?

Help Keep Your Money Organized and To Do A Health Check When Spending Cash

6. Why is it important to set aside a little "blow money" every month?

Cause This Is New and There Will Be Mistakes. This Is a cushion

PERSONAL APPLICATION

After viewing *Cash Flow Planning*, be sure to complete these action items before moving on to the next lesson.

- Complete your first monthly zero-based budget using the Monthly Cash Flow Plan form in the back of this workbook or in the online resources.

- Complete these additional forms in the back of this workbook or in the online resources:

  - Major Components of a Healthy Financial Plan
  - Consumer Equity Sheet
  - Income Sources
  - Lump Sum Payment Planning

DUMPING *debt*

BREAKING THE CHAINS OF DEBT

Debt is the most successfully, aggressively marketed product in history. *What? Debt isn't a product, is it?* You bet it is. And it isn't just sold by banks and credit card companies anymore. Many national retail chains make more money on the sale of credit applications than they do on the actual merchandise they sell.

In *Dumping Debt*, Dave blows the lid off the credit game, debunking the leading myths about debt that have become ingrained in our natural way of thinking. Then he walks you right out of debt with his simple, clear and effective debt snowball technique.

DUMPING debt

▶ **Video 1:** A History of Debt

DEBUNKING THE MYTH

If you tell a lie or spread a ___Myth___ often enough, loud enough and long enough, the myth becomes accepted as ___Truth___.

Debt has been ___Marketed___ to us in so many forms and so aggressively since the 1960s that to even imagine living without it requires a complete ___Paradigm___ ___Shift___.

▶ **Video 2:** Debt Myths: Loans, Lottery and Car Payments

MYTH If I loan money to a friend or relative, I will be ___Helping___ them.

TRUTH The relationship will be strained or ___Destroyed___.

MYTH By _Co Signing_ a loan, I am helping out a friend or relative.

TRUTH The bank requires a co-signer because the person isn't likely to _Repay_. So be ready to pay the loan and have your credit damaged because you are on the loan.

WISDOM

"It's stupid to guarantee someone else's loan."

—*Proverb*

MYTH Cash advance, rent-to-own, title pawning and tote-the-note car lots are needed _Services_ for lower-income people to get ahead.

TRUTH These are horrible, _Greedy_ rip-offs that aren't needed and benefit no one but the owners of these companies.

MYTH Playing the lottery and other forms of gambling will make me _Rich_.

TRUTH The lottery is a tax on the poor and on people who can't do _Math_.

MYTH Car _Payment_ are a way of life, and you'll always have one.

TRUTH Staying away from car payments by driving reliable used cars is what the typical millionaire does. That is _How_ they became millionaires.

KEY POINT

If you do rich people stuff, you get rich.

If you do poor people stuff, you get poor.

It's really that simple.

"Another way to solve the traffic problems of this country is to pass a law that only paid-for cars be allowed to use the highways."

—Will Rogers

MYTH ___Leasing___ your car is what sophisticated financial people do. You should always lease things that go down in value. There are tax advantages.

TRUTH *Consumer Reports, Smart Money* magazine and a good calculator will tell you that the car lease is the most ___Expensive___ way to finance and operate a vehicle.

TRUTH If you own a business, you can write off your ___Paid-For___ car on taxes without paying payments for the privilege.

TRUTH The way to minimize the money lost on things that go down in value is to buy slightly ___used___.

MYTH You can get a good deal on a ___New___ car.

TRUTH A new car loses ___70___ % of its value in the first four years. This is the largest purchase most consumers make that goes down in value.

▶ **Video 3:** Debt Myths: Credit Cards and Mortgages

MYTH I'll take out a 30-year mortgage and pay ___15yr Extra___. I promise!

TRUTH Life happens! Something else will always seem more important, so almost no one pays extra every month. Never take more than a ___15yr___ fixed-rate loan.

30-Year vs. 15-Year Mortgage at 6%

Home Purchased		250,000
Down Payment		− 25,000
Mortgage Amount		$225,000

Payment	Total	Pay Back
30 years	$1,349	$485,636
15 years	$1,899	$341,762
Difference	$550	$143,874

You Save More Than $143,000!

MYTH It is wise to take out an _ARM_ or a _Balloon_ mortgage if "I know I'll be moving."

TRUTH You *will* be moving—when they _foreclose_.

> ## WISDOM
>
> *"The chief cause of failure and unhappiness is trading what you want most for what you want now."*
>
> —Zig Ziglar

MYTH You need a credit card to _Rent_ a car or to make _purchase_ online or by phone.

TRUTH A _Debit_ card will do all of that, except for a few major rental companies. Check in advance.

MYTH "I pay mine off every _month_ with no annual fee. I get brownie points, air miles and a free hat."

TRUTH When you use plastic instead of cash, you spend _12-18_ % more because spending cash hurts. So what if you get 1% back and a free hat?

MYTH I'll make sure my _teenager_ gets a credit card so he/she can learn to be responsible with money.

TRUTH Teens are a huge _target_ of credit card companies today.

MYTH The home equity loan is good for _Consolidation_ and is a substitute for an emergency fund.

TRUTH You don't go into _debt_ for emergencies.

MYTH Debt consolidation _Saves_ interest, and you get just one smaller payment.

TRUTH Debt consolidation is a _Con_.

TRUTH Debt consolidation typically saves _Little_ or _No_ interest because you will throw your low-interest loans into the deal.

TRUTH You can't _borrow_ your way out of debt.

Smaller payments equal more _time_ in debt.

Gazelle Intensity

"My son, if you have become surety for your friend, if you have shaken hands in pledge for a stranger, you are snared by the words of your mouth; you are taken by the words of your mouth.

So do this, my son, and deliver yourself; for you have come into the hand of your friend: go and humble yourself; plead with your friend.

Give no sleep to your eyes, nor slumber to your eyelids.

Deliver yourself like a gazelle from the hand of the hunter, and like a bird from the hand of the fowler."

—Proverbs

▶ Video 4: Gazelle Intensity!

MYTH Debt is a ___tool___ and should be used to create prosperity.

TRUTH The borrower is ___slave___ to the lender.

TRUTH When surveyed, the Forbes 400 were asked, "What is the most important key to building wealth?" ___75___ % replied that becoming and staying debt free was the number-one key to serious wealth building.

How much could you ___save___, invest, blow and ___Give___ if you had no payments?

STEPS OUT OF DEBT

1. Quit __*borrowing*__ more __*money*__!

2. You must __*Save*__ money.

3. __*Prayer*__ really works.

4. __*Sell*__ something.

5. Take a part-time __*Job*__ or __*overtime*__ (temporarily).

BABY STEP 2

Pay off all debt using the
__*Debt*__ __*Snowball*__

AMERICA'S *CREDIT REPORT*

The total American consumer debt is currently around **$2.5 TRILLION**

Credit card issuers mail more than **5 BILLION OFFERS** to people every year *and send untold millions or billions more by email!*

181 MILLION people in the U.S. have at least one credit card. *That represents 77% of the adult population.*

Over **1.4 BILLION** credit cards are in circulation in America. *That means every cardholder has an average of 7.7 cards!*

46% of cardholders make only minimum payments *and carry a balance on their credit cards every month.*

Over the last 20 years, outstanding credit-card debt has increased by **229%**

OUTSTANDING CREDIT CARD DEBT

Of cardholding households that carry a balance, the average credit card debt is almost

$16,000

It would take more than

30 YEARS

to pay this off with only minimum payments at the average interest rate ...
AND THAT'S IF YOU DON'T CHARGE ANYTHING ELSE!

DEBT SNOWBALL

Now it's time to knock out that debt! List your debts in order, from the smallest balance to the largest. Don't be concerned with interest rates, unless two debts have a similar payoff balance. In that case, list the one with the higher interest rate first. As you start eliminating debts, you'll start to build some serious momentum. These quick wins will keep you motivated, so you'll be able to stay on track.

The idea of the snowball is simple: Pay minimum payments on all of your debts except for the smallest one. Then, attack that one with gazelle intensity! Every extra dollar you can get your hands on should be thrown at that smallest debt until it is gone. Then, you attack the second one. Every time you pay a debt off, you add its old minimum payment to your next debt payments. So, as the snowball rolls over, it picks up more snow. Get it?

Redo this sheet every time you pay off a debt so that you can see how close you're getting to total debt freedom. Keep the old sheets for encouragement—or to wallpaper the bathroom in your debt-free house someday!

The "New Payment" is the total of the previous debt's payment PLUS the current debt's minimum. As these payments compound, you'll start making huge payments as you work down the list until you can eventually call Dave's radio show and scream, "I'M DEBT FREE!"

10 DEBT SNOWBALL

Item	Total Payoff	Minimum Payment	New Payment
JC Penney	$150	$15	(Garage Sale)
Sears	$250	$10	$25
Visa	$500	$75	$100
MasterCard	$1,500	$90	$190
Car	$4,000	$210	$400
Student Loan	$4,000	$65	$465

Go online to take your quiz for *Dumping Debt*!

BABY STEPS

Here's a review of the Baby Step covered in this lesson:

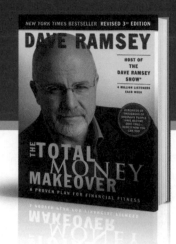

 Pay off all debt using the debt snowball.
For more insight, see Chapter 7 of
The Total Money Makeover.

ANSWER KEY

Myth	Month
Truth	12–18
Marketed	Teenager
Paradigm Shift	Target
Helping	Consolidation
Destroyed	Debt
Co-Signing	Saves
Repay	Con
Services	Little
Greedy	No
Rich	Borrow
Math	Time
Payments	Tool
How	Slave
Leasing	75
Expensive	Save
Paid-For	Give
Used	Borrowing
New	Money
70	Save
Extra	Prayer
15-year	Sell
ARM	Job
Balloon	Overtime
Foreclose	Debt Snowball
Rent	
Purchases	
Debit	

KEY POINTS

1. Debt has only become accepted as normal in America over the last 20 years or so.

2. Credit cards can absolutely destroy your financial life.

3. Gazelle intensity is the key to getting out of debt.

4. The debt snowball pays off your debts smallest to largest, according to account balance.

QUESTIONS FOR REFLECTION

1. How old were you when you got your first credit card? How did that make you feel (at the time)?

_____

_____

2. What would it feel like to have absolutely no debt?

_____

_____

3. What would you do with your income if you didn't have any debt payments?

_____

_____

4. Have you ever believed or spread any of the myths covered in this lesson? Which ones?

_____

_____

5. Why is "gazelle intensity" so important in getting out of debt?

_____

_____

6. What is your reaction to the phrase "the borrower is slave to the lender"?

_____

_____

PERSONAL APPLICATION

After viewing *Dumping Debt*, be sure to complete these action items before moving on to the next lesson.

- Complete the Debt Snowball form in the back of this workbook or in the online resources.

- Complete the Credit Card History form in the back of this workbook or in the online resources. Use this as a guide to begin closing your open credit card accounts.

- Optional: Read Chapters 3, 4 and 7 of *The Total Money Makeover*.

201

PLANNING FOR THE FUTURE

UNDER STANDING *insurance*

CLAUSE AND EFFECT

Insurance? Blech! This is a topic that few people really enjoy, and yet it is an area that impacts your finances more than you could possibly imagine! Can you explain how your life insurance works? If your spouse were suddenly widowed, how much would he or she need to survive? How does health insurance work? Are specialty plans, such as cancer policies, a good deal? Let's find out!

In *Understanding Insurance*, Dave walks you through the seven types of insurance that every adult needs, and he reveals how to avoid the traps in the insurance industry that can leave you—and your heirs—flat broke!

UNDER STANDING insurance

▶ **Video 1:** Insurance Basics: Homeowner's, Auto and Health

WISDOM

"A prudent man sees evil and hides himself, the naive proceed and pay the penalty."

—Old Testament

"There can be no real individual freedom in the presence of economic insecurity."

—Chester Bowles

INSURANCE BASICS

Insurance is an essential financial planning tool.

The purpose of insurance is to ___transfer___ risk.

Without proper insurance, certain losses can ___bankrupt___ you. Conventional wisdom says that you should transfer that risk.

BASIC TYPES OF COVERAGE NEEDED

1. Homeowner's or Renter's Insurance
2. Auto Insurance
3. Health Insurance
4. Disability Insurance
5. Long-Term Care Insurance
6. Identity Theft Protection
7. Life Insurance

TYPES OF INSURANCE

HOMEOWNER'S AND AUTO INSURANCE

If you have a full emergency fund, raise your

_____Deductable_____.

Carry adequate _____Liability_____. $500 Liability

Consider dropping your _____Collision_____ on older cars.   your car

Homeowner's insurance should be "guaranteed

_____Replacement_____ cost."

_____Umbrella_____ liability policies are a

good buy once you have some assets.

HEALTH INSURANCE

Keys to saving on your health premiums:

- Increase your _____Deductible_____

  and/or co-insurance amount.

- Increase your _____Stop_____ - _____Loss_____,

  but never decrease your maximum pay.

- See if an _____HSA_____, a Health Savings

  Account, would make sense for your situation.

- The HSA is a _____Tax_____ - _____Sheltered_____

  savings account for medical expenses that works

  with a high-deductible insurance policy.

> **KEY POINT**
>
> Medical debt is consistently one of the leading causes for personal bankruptcy.
>
> **You must have health insurance!**

DISABILITY INSURANCE

Disability insurance is designed to replace _Income_ lost due to a short-term or permanent disability.

Try to buy disability insurance that pays if you cannot perform the job that you were educated or _Trained_ to do.

That is called _Occupational_, or "own occ," disability. Many times, this is only available for two years.

Beware of _Short_-term policies covering less than _5_ years.

Buy IX with After Tax Dollars →

Your coverage should be for _65_ % of your current income.

The _Elimination_ period is the time between the disabling event and when the payments actually begin.

A _Longer_ elimination period will _Lower_ your premium cost.

LONG-TERM CARE INSURANCE *Do Not Buy Until 60 yrs of Age.*

Long-term care insurance is for __*Nursing*__
home, assisted living facilities or in-home care.

__*69*__ % of people over the age of 65 will require
long-term care at some point in their lives.

IDENTITY THEFT PROTECTION

Don't buy ID theft protection that only provides credit
report __*Monitoring*__ .

Good protection includes __*Restoration*__
services that assign a __*Counselor*__
to clean up the mess.

▶ Video 3: The Truth About Life Insurance

LIFE INSURANCE

Life insurance is designed to replace lost income due
to __*Death*__ .

Most people have no __*idea*__ what kind of
life insurance they __*own*__ .

Two Types of Life Insurance:

1. __*Term*__ insurance is for a specified
   period, is substantially cheaper, and has no
   savings plan built into it.
2. __*Cash*__ __*Value*__
   insurance is normally for life and is more *Permanent whole Life*
   expensive because it funds a savings plan.

WISDOM

"It is unwise to hope
for the best without
preparing for the
worst."

—Anonymous

KEY POINT

Human beings have a 100%
mortality rate—we're all going
to die someday. If people
depend on your income, it is
your responsibility to make
sure they'll be taken care of if
(or when) something
happens to you.

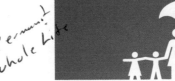

The most common insurance myth is that the need for life insurance is a ___permanent___ situation.

Twenty years from today, when the children are grown and gone, you are debt-free (including that 15-year mortgage), and you have investments that have grown to a substantial amount, you will have become self-___insured___.

WHY NOT LIFE INSURANCE AS AN INVESTMENT?

1. Returns are historically ___Low___.
2. When you die with cash value, the insurance company ___Keeps___ the cash value.
3. The ___Fees___ deducted from your return are extremely ___High___.

WHAT TO REMEMBER WHEN PURCHASING LIFE INSURANCE:

1. Buy only low-cost level ___Term___.
2. Do not forget your ___Spouse___.
3. Stay away from fancy ___options___.
4. Children only need enough for ___Burial___ expenses.

Cash Value vs. Term + Roth IRA

For $145 a month, you could have $125,000 in cash value insurance. Or, for that same $145, you could pay $10 for $400,000 in 20-year term insurance and invest $135 into a Roth IRA. If you start at age 30...

Age	$125,000 Cash Value Guaranteed	$135/mo in Roth 12% Return
50	$27,500	$133,000
70	$66,000	$1,500,000

You need about __10__ times your income. Invested at 10–12%, the annual interest would replace your lost income.

> **KEY POINT**
>
> Before you cancel your cash value policy, make sure that you already have a new term policy in place! If, for some reason, you cannot be approved for a new term policy, it is better to hang on to a bad cash value policy than to have nothing at all—until you become self-insured.

▶ **Video 4:** Insurance to Avoid

INSURANCE TO AVOID

1. ___Credit___ life and disability
2. Credit ___Card___ protection
3. ___Cancer___ and hospital indemnity
4. Accidental ___Death___
5. Any insurance with ___Cash___ ___Value___, investments or refunds
6. Pre-paid ___Burial___ policies
7. ___Mortgage___ life insurance
8. Any kind of ___Duplicate___ coverage

📷 Go online to take your quiz for *Understanding Insurance!*

NEXT STEPS

Something get your attention in this lesson? Write it down!

KEY POINTS

1. The seven major types of insurance you need are homeowner's (or renter's), auto, health, disability, long-term care (after age 60), identity theft and life.

2. Make insurance a priority in order to avoid a financial disaster.

3. Never use your insurance for saving or investing.

QUESTIONS FOR REFLECTION

1. What could happen to you financially if you do not have the proper amount of insurance in place?

   _____

   _____

2. How does having an emergency fund affect your insurance premiums and deductibles?

   _____

   _____

3. Why is it so important to make sure your homeowner's policy includes guaranteed replacement cost?

_____

_____

4. Why do you think so few people carry long-term disability coverage? Why is this so dangerous?

_____

_____

5. What is the difference between term and cash value life insurance?

_____

_____

6. What happens to your cash savings inside of a cash value life insurance plan when you die?

_____

_____

PERSONAL APPLICATION

After viewing *Understanding Insurance*, be sure to complete these action items before moving on to the next lesson.

- Complete the Insurance Coverage Recap form in the back of this workbook or in the online resources.

- Identify any insurance policies that need to be changed or added to your financial plan.

- Calculate how much life insurance coverage you need based on Dave's principles.

- Do a break-even analysis to see if a higher deductible makes sense on your various policies.

investing BASICS

OF MICE AND MUTUAL FUNDS

Stocks. Bonds. Mutual Funds. CDs. Annuities. Commodities. Diversification. Dividends. Let's be honest: For the average American, the area of investing can be scary, boring and intimidating. But without a fundamental understanding of what these things are and how they work, we run the risk of putting our hard-earned money into investments we don't understand.

In *Investing Basics*, Dave empowers you to make wise investing decisions. It's not as mystifying as you may think! You work hard for your money; let Dave show you how to make your money work hard for you!

investing BASICS

▶ Video 1: Ground Rules and Definitions

▶ Video 1: Ground Rules and Definitions

WISDOM

"Risk comes from not knowing what you're doing."

—Warren Buffett

"Give portions to seven, yes to eight, for you do not know what disaster may come upon the land."

—Old Testament

KEY POINT

Remember Grandma's advice: Don't put all your eggs in one basket.

KISS RULE OF INVESTING

Keep it __Simple__, __Stupid__!

It does not mean that you are stupid if you make __Simple__ investments.

Never invest purely for __tax__ __saving__.

Never invest using __borrowed__ money.

DIVERSIFICATION

Diversification means to __spread__ __around__.

Diversification __Lowers__ risk.

THE POWER OF DIVERSIFICATION

Two people make a one-time investment of $10,000 and leave it alone for 25 years. Investor 1 makes a single, undiversified investment of $10,000. Investor 2 invests the same $10,000 but diversifies his money across five different investments. How did they do?

Each person invests $10,000 and leaves it alone for 25 years

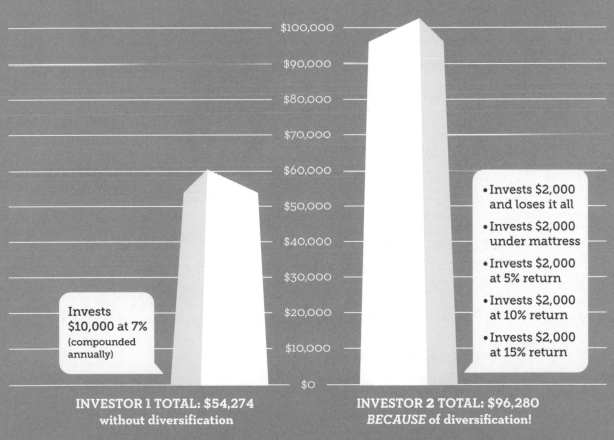

Invests $10,000 at 7% (compounded annually)

- Invests $2,000 and loses it all
- Invests $2,000 under mattress
- Invests $2,000 at 5% return
- Invests $2,000 at 10% return
- Invests $2,000 at 15% return

INVESTOR 1 TOTAL: $54,274
without diversification

INVESTOR 2 TOTAL: $96,280
BECAUSE of diversification!

A DIFFERENCE OF OVER
$42,000!

"October. This is one of the peculiarly dangerous months to speculate in stocks. The others are July, January, September, April, November, May, March, June, December, August and February."

—Mark Twain

RISK RETURN RATIO AND LIQUIDITY

With virtually all investments, as the ___Risk___ goes up, so does the potential ___Return___.

When discussing investments, liquidity is ___Availability___.

As there is more liquidity, there is typically ___Less___ return.

▶ Video 2: Types of Investing, Part 1

TYPES OF INVESTMENTS

MONEY MARKETS

A CD is a certificate of ___deposit___, typically at a bank.

Money market mutual funds are ___Low___-risk money market accounts with check-writing privileges. These are great for emergency funds.

SINGLE STOCKS

Single stock investing carries an extremely ___High___ degree of risk.

When you buy stock, you are buying a small piece of ___ownership___ in the company.

Your return comes as the company increases in ___Value___ or pays you, its owner, some of the profits (called ___Dividends___).

Standard Mutual Fund Diversification

Dave recommends dividing your investment dollars across these four types:

- 25% GROWTH (Mid Cap)
- 25% GROWTH & INCOME (Large Cap)
- 25% AGGRESSIVE GROWTH (Small Cap)
- 25% INTERNATIONAL

BONDS

A bond is a ___Debt___ instrument by which the company owes ___you___ money.

Your return is the fluctuation in price and the ___interest___ rate paid. ___Few___ individuals do well with single bond purchases.

MUTUAL FUNDS

Investors pool their ___money___ to invest.

Professional portfolio managers manage the pool or ___fund___.

Your ___return___ comes as the ___value___ of the fund is increased.

▶ **Video 3:** Types of Investing, Part 2

Mutual funds are good _____-term investments.

RENTAL REAL ESTATE

Least _____ consumer investment.

You should have a lot of _____ before using real estate as an investment.

ANNUITIES

Annuities are _____ accounts with an insurance company.

_____ annuities are at a low interest rate of around 5%, aren't really fixed, and are bad long-term investments.

_____ annuities are mutual funds sheltered by the annuity covering, thereby allowing the mutual fund to grow tax-deferred.

HORRIBLE INVESTMENTS
- Gold
- Commodities and Futures
- Day Trading
- Viaticals

CONCLUSION

If you do not understand an investment well enough to teach someone else how it works, DON'T BUY IT!

Build wealth slowly.

 Go online to take your quiz for *Investing Basics*!

MONTHLY DEBT PAYMENTS
ROB YOU OF YOUR RETIREMENT

Years Invested Monthly At 12% Per Year

MONTHLY PAYMENTS	5 YEARS	10 YEARS	15 YEARS	25 YEARS	40 YEARS
$100	8,167	23,004	49,958	187,885	1,176,477
$200	16,334	46,008	99,916	375,769	2,352,954
$300	24,500	69,012	149,874	563,654	3,529,431
$400	32,668	92,015	199,832	751,538	4,705,909
$500	40,835	115,019	249,790	939,423	5,882,386
$600	49,002	138,023	299,748	1,127,308	7,058,863
$700	57,168	161,027	349,706	1,315,193	8,235,341
$800	65,336	184,031	399,664	1,503,077	9,411,818
$900	73,503	207,034	449,622	1,690,962	10,588,295
$1,000	81,669	230,039	499,580	1,878,847	11,764,772
$1,200	98,004	276,046	599,496	2,254,616	14,117,727
$1,500	122,504	345,058	749,370	2,818,270	17,647,159
$2,000	163,339	460,077	999,160	3,757,693	23,529,545

HOWEVER, RETIREMENT CAN LOOK PRETTY SWEET IF YOU DON'T HAVE ANY DEBT.

NEXT STEPS

Something get your attention in this lesson? Write it down!

_____

_____

_____

_____

_____

ANSWER KEY

Simple	Value
Stupid	Dividends
Simple	Debt
Tax	You
Savings	Interest
Borrowed	Few
Spread	Money
Around	Fund
Lowers	Return
Risk	Value
Return	Long
Availability	Liquid
Less	Cash
Deposit	Savings
Low	Fixed
High	Variable
Ownership	

KEY POINTS

1. The key to successful investing is to diversify and do the same simple things over and over again.

2. Do not let a "financial guy" make your decisions for you. Only work with advisors who have the heart of a teacher and will teach you how to make your own decisions.

3. Never borrow money to invest—including real estate investment properties.

QUESTIONS FOR REFLECTION

1. Why is investing intimidating to many people?

   _____

   _____

2. Why is it dangerous to invest with borrowed money?

   _____

   _____

3. Why is diversification important?

   _____

   _____

4. Why are single stocks so dangerous?

_____

_____

5. Why does Dave stress the importance of becoming debt-free (except the mortgage) before you begin your long-term investing?

_____

_____

6. Why is it so important to make your own educated, well-informed decisions, rather than simply surrendering your decisions to an advisor?

_____

_____

7. Why is it important for spouses to be on the same page when it comes to dumping debt and investing?

_____

_____

PERSONAL APPLICATION

After viewing *Investing Basics*, be sure to complete these action items before moving on to the next lesson.

- Calculate how much your debt payments are robbing from your retirement (see page 89).

- Optional: Read Chapter 5 of *The Total Money Makeover*.

- Review the funds and types of investments currently in your investing portfolio, making sure you're still confident in your choices.

Retirement
PLANNING

FROM FRUITION TO TUITION

Just picture it: You're out of debt and you have an emergency fund of three to six months of expenses sitting in the bank. Now it's time to build some wealth for your future!

In *Retirement Planning*, Dave helps you understand all those initials and abbreviations: IRA, 401(k), 403(b), 457, SEPP and more! Plus, he shows you the best way to make sure your kids get through college without a student loan—what an idea!

Retirement PLANNING

▶ Video 1: Retirement Plan Options

RETIREMENT & COLLEGE FUNDING

Once the emergency fund is in place, you should begin retirement and college funding, which falls within long-term investing for _____.

BABY STEP ④

Invest __15__ % of your household income into Roth IRAs and pre-tax retirement plans.

ALWAYS save long-term with tax - _favored_ dollars.

Tax-favored means that the investment is in a _Qualified_ _Plan_ or has special tax treatment.

QUALIFIED PLANS

- Individual Retirement Arrangement (IRA)
- Simplified Employee Pension Plan (SEPP)
- 401(k), 403(b), 457

INDIVIDUAL RETIREMENT ARRANGEMENT (IRA)

Everyone with an ___Earned___ income is eligible.

The maximum annual contribution for income earners and non-income producing spouses is $ ___5000___ as of 2011.

Remember: IRA is not a type of ___investment___ at a bank. It is the *tax treatment* on virtually any type of investment.

ROTH IRA

The Roth IRA is an ___After___-tax IRA that grows tax ___free___!

If you ___save___ like we teach, you should use the Roth IRA.

WISDOM

"A good man leaves an inheritance for his children's children."

—Proverbs

"Most people have the will to win; few have the will to prepare to win."

—Bobby Knight

KEY POINT

The Roth IRA has specific eligibility requirements:

Singles—100% contribution with income less than $110,000. Phase out between $110,000–125,000. Not eligible above $125,000.

Married filing jointly—100% contribution with income less than $173,000. Phase out between $173,000–183,000. Not eligible over $183,000.

WHY THE ROTH IRA?

1. More __Choices__
2. Higher __Bracket__ at retirement
3. More __invested__
4. More __flexibility__

FLEXIBILITY:

Tax-free and penalty-free withdrawals at any time equal to contributions. After the emergency fund is depleted, you have a fallback.

After five years, you can make tax-free, penalty-free withdrawals of 100% under these conditions:

1. Over 59 and a half years old
2. Because of death or disability
3. First-time home purchase (max $10,000)

SIMPLIFIED EMPLOYEE PENSION PLAN (SEPP)

A __self__-employed person may deduct up to __15__% of their net profit on the business by investing in a SEPP.

As of 2010, the maximum deductible amount is the smaller of $49,000 or 25% of the participant's contribution. All employees who have been with the firm more than three of the last five years must receive the same percentage of their pay.

401(K), 403(B) & 457 RETIREMENT PLANS

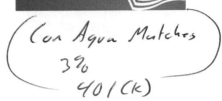

Con Agua Matches 3% 401(Ck)

Most companies have completely done away with traditional _Pension_ plans in the last 10-20 years. Some new plans offer a variety of pre-tax choices.

Some companies are now offering the _roth_ 401(k), which grows tax-free.

Do not use a Guaranteed Investment _Contract_ (GIC) or bond funds to fund your plan.

You should be funding your plan whether your company _Matches_ or not, but the plans that have company matching provide even greater returns.

▶ **Video 2:** Rollovers and Thrift Plan Suggestions

ROLLOVERS

You should _Always_ roll all retirement plans to an IRA when you _Leave_ the company.

Do not bring the money home! Make it a _Direct Transfer_.

You should roll to a Roth IRA ONLY if:

1. You will have saved over $ *700,000*
   by age 65.

2. You pay your taxes _Out_ of _Pocket_
   and not from the IRA funds.

3. You understand that all taxes will become due on the rollover amount.

RETIREMENT LOANS

Never _Borrow_ against your retirement plan.

FEDERAL THRIFT PLAN

If you are a federal government worker and have the standard thrift plan, we recommend _60_ % in the C Fund, _20_ % in the S Fund and _20_ % in the I Fund.

OUR SUGGESTION

HOW TO FUND YOUR 15%:

ConAgra 390

1. Fund 401(k) or other employer plans up to the _Match_ (if applicable).

Today Max 5,000

2. Above the matched amount, fund _Roth_ IRAs. If there is no match, start with Roth IRAs.

3. Complete 15% of your income by going back to your _(401(k))_ or other company plans.

Note: This is the best plan if you end up with $700,000 or more by age 65, because mandatory retirement withdrawals will cause a higher tax bracket at retirement.

DREAM
with me...

Imagine if ...

A 30-year-old couple partially funds a Roth IRA ($500 per month) at 12%. At 70 years old they will have...

$5,882,386

TAX FREE!

Imagine if ...

That same 30-year-old couple made $40,000 and saved 15% in a 401(k) ($500 per month) at 12%. At 70 years old they will have...

$5,882,386

Now, imagine if ...

That 30-year-old couple—DEBT FREE—does both, saving $1,000 per month at 12%. At 70 years old, they will have ...

$11,764,772!

BABY STEP ⑤

Save for your children's __College__ using tax-favored plans.

FIRST ...

Save in an Education Savings Account (ESA), or "Education __IRA__."

- You may save $2,000 (after tax) per year, per child, that grows tax free! If you start when your child is born and save $2,000 a year for 18 years, you would only invest a total of $36,000. However, at 12% growth, your child would have $126,000 for college—TAX FREE!

ABOVE THAT ...

If you want to save more or if you don't meet the income limits for an ESA, use a certain type of __529__ plan.

- The only type we recommend is one that leaves __you__ in control of the mutual fund at all times.

- Never buy a plan that:
    1. __Freezes__ your options.
    2. Automatically changes your investments based on the __age__ of the child.

ONLY THEN ...

Move to an _____UTMA_____ or _____UGMA_____ plan.

- While this is one way to save with reduced taxes, it is _____NOT_____ as good as the other options.

- UTMA/UGMA stands for Uniform _____Transfer_____ / Gift to Minors Act.

- The account is _____Listed_____ in the child's name and a _____Custodian_____ is named, usually the parent or grandparent. This person is the manager until the child reaches age 21. At age 21 (age 18 for UGMA), they can do with it as they please.

THREE "NEVERS" OF COLLEGE SAVING

1. Never save for college using _____Insurance_____.
2. Never save for college using _____Saving_____ bonds. (Only earns 5-6%.)
3. Never save for college using _____Prepaid_____ college tuition. (Only earns 7% inflation rate.)

Go online to take your quiz for *Retirement Planning*!

12 MONTHLY RETIREMENT PLANNING

Too many people use the READY-FIRE-AIM approach to retirement planning. That's a bad plan. You need to aim first. Your assignment is to determine how much per month you should be saving at 12% interest in order to retire at 65 with the amount you need.

If you save at 12% and inflation is at 4%, then you are moving ahead of inflation at a net of 8% per year. If you invest your nest egg at retirement at 12% and want to break even with 4% inflation, you will be living on 8% income.

Step 1: Annual income (today) you wish to retire on: _____50,000_____

Divide by .08

(Nest egg needed) equals: _____625,000_____

Step 2: To achieve that nest egg, you will save at 12%, netting 8% after inflation. So, we will target that nest egg using 8%.

Nest Egg Needed $ _____625,000_____

Multiply by Factor (Starting at Age 30)   X _____.000436_____

Monthly Savings Needed   = _____$272.⁵⁰_____

Note: Be sure to try one or two examples if you wait 5 or 10 years to start.

8% FACTORS (SELECT THE ONE THAT MATCHES YOUR AGE)

YOUR AGE	YEARS TO SAVE	FACTOR	YOUR AGE	YEARS TO SAVE	FACTOR
25	40	.000286	45	20	.001698
30	35	.000436	50	15	.002890
35	30	.000671	55	10	.005466
40	25	.001051	60	5	.013610

In order to have enough for college, you must aim at something. Your assignment is to determine how much per month you should be saving at 12% interest in order to have enough for college.

If you save at 12% and inflation is at 4%, then you are moving ahead of inflation at a net of 8% per year.

Step 1: In today's dollars, the annual cost of the college of your choice is:

Amount per year $ __20,000__

X 4 years = $ __80,000__

(hint: $15,000 to $25,000 annually)

Step 2: To achieve that college nest egg, you will save at 12%, netting 8% after inflation. So, we will target that nest egg using 8%.

Nest Egg Needed $ __80,000__

Multiply by Factor (Child is 4 years old) X __.003247__

Monthly Savings Needed = __$262.⁹⁶__

Note: Be sure to try one or two examples if you wait 5 or 10 years to start.

8% FACTORS (SELECT THE ONE THAT MATCHES YOUR CHILD'S AGE)

CHILD'S AGE	YEARS TO SAVE	FACTOR	CHILD'S AGE	YEARS TO SAVE	FACTOR
0	18	.002083	8	10	.005466
2	16	.002583	10	8	.007470
4	14	.003247	12	6	.010867
6	12	.004158	14	4	.017746

BABY STEPS

Here's a review of the Baby Steps covered in this lesson:

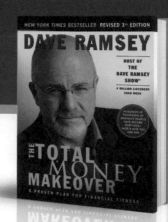

 4 *Invest 15% of your household income into Roth IRAs and pre-tax retirement plans.*
For more insight, see Chapter 9 of *The Total Money Makeover.*

 5 *Save for your children's college using tax-favored plans.*
For more insight, see Chapter 10 of *The Total Money Makeover.*

ANSWER KEY

Wealth	Out
15	Pocket
Favored	Borrow
Qualified Plan	60
Earned	20
5,000	20
Investment	Match
After	Roth
Free	401(k)
Save	College
Choices	IRA
Bracket	529
Invested	You
Flexibility	Freezes
Self	Age
15	UTMA
Pension	UGMA
Roth	Not
Contract	Transfer
Matches	Listed
Always	Custodian
Leave	Insurance
Direct Transfer	Savings
700,000	Pre-paid

KEY POINTS

1. The quality of your retirement is completely up to you. Do not count on Social (In)Security!

2. You should have your personal retirement contributions in place before saving for your children's college expenses.

3. If you do not have a will, get one today!

QUESTIONS FOR REFLECTION

1. What motivates you to get serious about your retirement plan? What type of retirement do you expect for yourself?

   _____

   _____

2. Should you ever temporarily stop adding to your retirement plan? If so, why? When should you resume?

   _____

   _____

3. Why is it such a bad idea to cash in or borrow against a retirement plan in order to get out of debt?

_____

_____

4. Why do you think college funding comes after retirement planning in the Baby Steps?

_____

_____

5. Would you feel guilty taking care of your own retirement plan before putting money aside for your child's college?

_____

_____

6. How does living by a monthly budget help you prepare for retirement?

_____

_____

PERSONAL APPLICATION

After viewing *Retirement Planning*, be sure to complete these action items before moving on to the next lesson.

- Complete the Monthly Retirement Planning and Monthly College Planning (if applicable) forms in the back of this workbook or in the online resources.

- Schedule a time to speak with an HR representative if you have questions about company-sponsored retirement plans.

- Optional: Read Chapters 9 and 10 of *The Total Money Makeover*.

REAL ESTATE AND MORTGAGES

LIVING THE AMERICAN DREAM

Homeownership is one of the biggest blessings we could ever experience. However, learning to navigate through the minefield of real estate and mortgages can be pretty daunting. With 40-year loans, interest-only options and reverse mortgages on the market, it's more important than ever to learn the ins and outs of personal real estate.

In *Real Estate and Mortgages*, Dave shares his most effective tips for buying and selling your home, and he breaks down the different mortgage options to reveal the best—and worst—ways to finance a house.

REAL ESTATE AND MORTGAGES

▶ Video 1: Selling Your Home

BABY STEP ⑥

Pay off your home _____.

SELLING A HOME

When selling a home, you should think like a _____.

The home should be in "near-perfect" condition.

The return on investment of fix-up dollars is _____.

The most important aspect of preparation is attention to the _____ appeal.

When selling your home, make sure that it is listed on the _____.

When selling, statistical research has found that the best real estate agents are worth _____ than they cost.

The exposure through the _____ Listing Service is worth it.

When selecting an agent, do not rely on _____ or _____.

These are professionals. You should always _____ them.

Offering a home _____ will typically not make a sale. If the buyer asks for a warranty, then consider it with that offer.

BUYING A HOME

Homeownership is a great investment for three main reasons:

1. It's a _____ savings plan.

2. It's an _____ hedge.

3. It grows virtually _____ - _____.

> **KEY POINT**
>
> You can have a gain of $250,000 single or $500,000 married and pay zero tax on the sale of your personal residence if you hold it at least two years.

> **WISDOM**
>
> "A man builds a fine house; and now he has a master, and a task for life; he is to furnish, watch, show it, and keep it in repair the rest of his days."
>
> —Ralph Waldo Emerson

Title insurance insures you against an _____ title, which is when your proper ownership is in question. It is a good buy.

Always get a land _____ if buying more than a standard subdivision lot.

Agents' access to the _____ system can make house hunting easier, but be careful. Many agents can only think like retailers, which is not what you want when buying.

WHAT TO BUY

Buy in the _____ price range of the neighborhood.

Homes appreciate in good neighborhoods and are priced based on three things: _____, _____ and _____!

If possible, buy near _____ or with a _____.

Buy bargains by _____ bad landscaping, outdated carpet, ugly wallpaper and the Elvis print in the master bedroom.

Why choose a 15-year mortgage?

(Figures based on 6% APR)

$225,000	15 years	Pay	$1,899 /mo
$225,000	30 years	Pay	$1,349 /mo
		Difference	$550 /mo

But after 10 years...

The 15-year loan has a balance of $98,210 while the 30-year loan has a balance of $188,292! During that 10 years, you would have paid almost $162,000 on the 30-year mortgage, but only paid down the loan by $36,708!

However ...

Always buy a home that is (or can be) attractive from the _____ and has a good basic _____.

Have the home inspected mechanically and structurally by a certified _____

_____.

Appraisals are an "_____ of value," but it's a better opinion than the current homeowner has. Always order one if in doubt.

WHAT NOT TO BUY

1. _____ or _____ _____

2. _____

▶ **Video 3:** Understanding Your Mortgage Options

MORTGAGES

First, remember to _____ debt.

The best mortgage is the _____% down plan.

But if you must take a mortgage ...

Do not buy until you are ready. That means you are out of debt with a fully funded emergency fund.

There is nothing wrong with _____ for a little while. This demonstrates _____ and wisdom.

Get a payment of no more than _____% of your take-home pay on a _____ fixed-rate loan, with at least _____% down. Have a fully funded emergency fund left over after closing.

KEY POINT

To calculate how an ARM adjusts, see "How to Figure the Change in Your ARM" at the end of this lesson.

Where's the tax advantage?

Mortgage Amount	Interest Rate	Annual Interest Paid
$200,000	5%	$10,000

Mortgage interest is tax-deductible, so you would not have to pay taxes on this $10,000. That is why many people tell you to keep the mortgage. But what does this really save you?

Taxable Amount	Tax Bracket	Annual Taxes Paid
$10,000	25%	$2,500

So, if you keep your mortgage just for the "tax advantages," all you are really doing is sending $10,000 to the bank instead of sending $2,500 to the IRS. Where's the "advantage" in that?

HORRIBLE MORTGAGE OPTIONS

1. Adjustable Rate Mortgages (ARMs) were brought on with the advent of _____ interest rates in the early 1980s.

   - The concept of the ARM is to _____ the risk of higher interest rates to the _____ and, in return, the lender gives a lower rate up front.

   - Of course, _____ - _____ loans are a bad idea because you are only paying the interest—duh!

   - You can qualify for more home with ARMs, but the risk of financial stress later is not worth it.

KEY POINT

The FTC says that reverse mortgage options have the most fraud in the mortgage business.

2. _____ Mortgages

   - Bad idea because you are putting a paid-for home at risk and the fees are horrible.

3. _____, or Bi-Weekly Payoff

   - Allows you to make a half-payment every two weeks, which equals 13 payments a year. Therefore, the reason it pays off early is because you make one extra payment a year.

   - Do not pay a fee for this option. You can easily do this on your own.

4. _____ Advantages of a Mortgage

   - Do not fall for the "tax advantage" myth that says you should keep your mortgage simply for the tax advantages. The math doesn't work.

BASIC WAYS TO FINANCE A HOME

1. _____, usually through FNMA and privately insured against default.

   - Down payments range from 5% to 20% or more.

   - These loans are available in all forms and formats.

   - PMI is _____ mortgage insurance.

2. _____, which is insured by HUD through the federal government.

   - Down payments are as low as _____% and are used on lower-priced homes.

   - These loans are currently _____ expensive than conventional financing and should be avoided.

3. _____, which is insured by the Veterans Administration.

   - Designed to benefit the veteran; the seller pays everything, allowing a true zero-down purchase.

   - With a good down payment, the conventional loan is a _____ deal.

4. _____ financing is when you pay the owner over time, making him/her the mortgage holder.

   - This is a _____ way to finance, because you can be creative in the structure of the loan.

Go online to take your quiz for *Real Estate and Mortgages*!

HOW TO FIGURE YOUR NEW PAYMENT

Use this worksheet to estimate the monthly mortgage payment on a 15-year loan compared to a 30-year loan.

_____ / 1,000 = _____ X _____ = _____
SALES PRICE   #1000'S   FACTOR   MONTHLY PAYMENT

Example: Sales Price - $150,000, 15 years at 6%

$150,000 / 1,000 = __150__ X __8.44__ = __$1,266__
SALES PRICE   #1000'S   FACTOR   MONTHLY PAYMENT

MONTHLY PAYMENT PER $1,000 IN LOAN AMOUNT

RATE	15-YEAR	30-YEAR	RATE	15-YEAR	30-YEAR
4.5%	7.65	5.07	8.5%	9.85	7.69
5.0%	7.91	5.37	9.0%	10.15	8.05
5.5%	8.17	5.68	9.5%	10.44	8.41
6.0%	8.44	6.00	10.0%	10.75	8.78
6.5%	8.71	6.32	10.5%	11.05	9.15
7.0%	8.99	6.66	11.0%	11.37	9.52
7.5%	9.28	7.00	11.5%	11.68	9.90
8.0%	9.56	7.34	12.0%	12.00	10.29

SHOULD I REFINANCE?

This worksheet helps you decide whether or not it would make sense to refinance your current mortgage to a lower-interest loan.

_____ — _____ = _____

Current principal and interest payment (not including taxes & insurance)　　　New principal and interest payment　　　Monthly savings

_____ / _____ = _____

Total closing costs　　　Monthly savings　　　Number of months to break even

Will you stay in your home longer than the number of months to break even? If so, you are a candidate for a refinance.

Example: Refinance on a $150,000 Mortgage at 8% to 6.5%

$1,434 current payment – $1,307 new payment = $127 savings

$2,300 closing cost divided by $127 savings = 18 months

ESTIMATED CLOSING COSTS TABLE

Loan Amount	Closing Costs	Loan Amount	Closing Costs	Loan Amount	Closing Costs
30,000	1,500	60,000	1,775	90,000	1,950
35,000	1,550	65,000	1,800	95,000	1,975
40,000	1,600	70,000	1,825	100,000	2,000
45,000	1,650	75,000	1,850	150,000	2,300
50,000	1,700	80,000	1,900	200,000	2,600
55,000	1,725	85,000	1,925	250,000	2,900

HOW TO FIGURE THE CHANGE IN YOUR ARM

Your Adjustable Rate Mortgage (ARM) adjusts based on the movement of an index. You can find your index in your original note or mortgage. The most commonly used index is the Treasury Bill (T-Bill). The one-year ARM uses the one-year T-Bill, the three-year ARM uses the three-year T-Bill, and so on. Other commonly used indexes are the LIBOR and the 11th District Cost of Funds.

1. First, find out what index you use and when it is adjusted.

2. Next, find out (also from your loan paperwork) what margin was assigned to your loan (usually 2.59).

Basically, your ARM adjusts as the index moves.

The index is usually published daily in The Wall Street Journal.

If you have a one-year ARM that adjusts with the one-year T-Bill and a margin of 2.59 (which is typical), then, at the one-year anniversary of your closing, you would look up the one-year T-Bill in The Wall Street Journal. Add the T-Bill to your margin, and you have your new rate (if it is not capped).

Example: T-Bill 4.41 plus margin 2.59 = 7% new interest rate.

Name of Index
Used by Your ARM:_____   Index Adjustment   _____

Date That It Is Adjusted:_____   Margin   _____

New Interest Rate   _____

WARNING: Almost all ARMs start below margin the first year, guaranteeing a payment increase at anniversary unless rates DROP.

BABY STEPS

Here's a review of the Baby Step covered in this lesson:

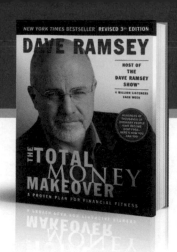

 Pay off your home early.
For more insight, see Chapter 11 of
The Total Money Makeover.

ANSWER KEY

Early	Trailers
Retailer	Mobile
Enormous	Homes
Curb	Timeshares
Internet	Hate
More	100
Multiple	Renting
Friendships	Patience
Relatives	25
Interview	15-year
Warranty	10
Forced	High
Inflation	Transfer
Tax Free	Borrower
Unclean	Interest
Survey	Only
MLS	Reverse
Bottom	Accelerated
Location	Tax
Location	Conventional
Location	Private
Water	FHA
View	3
Overlooking	More
Street	VA
Floor Plan	Better
Home	Owner
Inspector	Great
Opinion	

KEY POINTS

1. Think like a retailer when selling a home and like an investor when buying a home.

2. If a mortgage is necessary, only get a 15-year fixed mortgage with at least 10% down. Your payment should be less than 25% of your take-home pay.

3. The best mortgage is the 100% down plan!

QUESTIONS FOR REFLECTION

1. What does it mean to be "house poor"?

   _____

   _____

2. Is it ever okay to rent for a while? Why or why not?

   _____

   _____

3. What are the dangers in 30-year mortgages, adjustable rate loans and home equity loans?

   _____

   _____

4. Why are reverse mortgages such a bad idea?

_____

_____

5. According to Dave's recommended guidelines for personal mortgages, how much house can you actually afford?

_____

_____

6. How would paying off your home early make you feel? How would it affect your retirement?

_____

_____

PERSONAL APPLICATION

After viewing *Real Estate and Mortgages*, be sure to complete these action items before moving on to the next lesson.

- If you're currently in a 30-year mortgage, do some research to see if refinancing to a shorter-term loan makes sense. If not, figure out a new payment for yourself that would pay off your loan as though it were on a 15-year plan.

- If you are currently in any type of adjustable rate mortgage, get out of it immediately! Refinance into a 15-year fixed.

- Optional: Read Chapters 11 and 12 of *The Total Money Makeover*.

SECTION
301
PROTECTING YOUR MONEY

The four lessons in Section 301 are provided as a personal self-study option.

CREDIT BUREAUS & collections

CREDIT SHARKS IN SUITS

We live in a culture that bows down and worships at the altar of the almighty credit score, and it seems like we'll do anything to protect that little number. But what does the credit score really mean? What does it measure? The answer will surprise you!

In *Credit Bureaus and Collections*, Dave shows you exactly how the credit score is calculated and what it actually says about you. He will also walk you through common collection practices and strategies for dealing with collectors. Even if you never face these nagging calls yourself, chances are someone you love will!

CREDIT BUREAUS & collections

▶ **Video 1:** Credit 101: Scores, Reports and Identity Theft

CREDIT SCORE

MYTH You need to take out a credit card or car loan to "build up your _____ _____."

TRUTH The FICO score is an "I love _____" score and is not a measure of _____ financially.

CREDIT BUREAUS

Account information is removed from your credit report _____ years after the last activity on that account, except for a Chapter 7 bankruptcy, which stays on for _____ years.

Beware of credit clean-up scams. The only information that may be legally removed from a credit report is _____ information.

KEY POINT

With a 20% down payment on a reasonable house, two years or more on the job, and two years of paying your landlord early, you will qualify for a mortgage.

Don't fall for the lie!

FICO stands for Fair Isaac Corporation, which developed a score-based rating system that many companies use to measure an individual's credit risk.

While this measurement has become widely accepted, it is a faulty standard that is based on debt, not wealth.

The National Association of State Public Interest Research Groups (U.S. PIRG) did a survey of 200 adults in 30 states who checked their credit report for accuracy.

- _____% of those credit reports contained mistakes of some kind and _____% of them contained errors serious enough to result in the denial of credit.

- _____% of the credit reports contained credit accounts that had been closed by the consumer but incorrectly remained listed as open.

- _____% listed the same mortgage or loan twice.

You should check your credit report _____, which you can now do for free.

IDENTITY THEFT

What To Do:

1. Place a _____ _____ alert on your credit bureau report (stays on for 90 days without a police report).

2. Get a _____ _____.

3. Remember, this is _____. You owe _____ and should pay _____.

4. Contact the fraud victim _____ of each creditor and furnish _____.

5. Be _____—this will take some time. You now have a new _____.

> **KEY POINT**
>
> Of all the identity theft victims who call in to *The Dave Ramsey Show* for help and advice on this subject, approximately one-half know the person who stole their identities. The thief is often a friend or a family member.

CORRECTING CREDIT REPORT INACCURACIES

An updated version of the 1977 Federal Fair Credit Reporting Act requires a credit bureau to _____ all inaccuracies within 30 days of notification.

To clean your credit report of inaccurate information, you should write a separate letter for each inaccuracy, staple a copy of your credit report to each letter, and circle the account number.

Note: You should also request that "inquiries" be removed. All of these letters should be sent _____ mail with return receipt requested to prove when they receive the letter. If the credit bureau does not prove the accuracy of the account within 30 days, you should request they remove the _____ account from your file.

You will have to be assertive after the 30-day period.

Lodge any _____ with the Federal Trade Commission and your state's Consumer Affairs Division.

COLLECTION PRACTICES

The best way to pay debts is with a _____.

A collector's job is not to help your overall situation.
His only job is to get your _____.

Collectors are trained _____
or _____.

They are typically low-paid positions with
high _____.

They are taught in their training to evoke
strong _____.

The way to counteract this technique is to ALWAYS
pay _____ first, and then
_____ set the order of payment.

FEDERAL FAIR DEBT COLLECTION PRACTICES ACT

In 1977, a consumer law was passed by Congress called the Federal Fair Debt Collection Practices Act to protect you from unfair collectors. The law technically only applies to collection agencies (not your creditor), but later court cases make most creditors also abide by the FFDCPA.

- The Act states that harassment is illegal and restricts a collector's calls to between the hours of _____ and _____ (unless they have your permission).

- The Act also allows you to demand that a creditor cease calling you at _____. You should request this in writing by certified mail with return receipt requested.

- The Act even allows you to insist that a creditor stop _____ contact except to notify you of _____ proceedings.

- Do not use a cease-and-desist letter except in horrible situations, because all _____ stop and any hope of a positive resolution is lost.

Remember the Four Walls

No matter how tight your budget gets, never lose sight of these four priorities:

1. FOOD
2. SHELTER
3. CLOTHING
4. TRANSPORTATION

- No collector or creditor may _____ a bank account or garnish (attach) _____ without proper and lengthy court action, except in the case of delinquent IRS or student loan debt. All such threats are a bluff.

▶ Video 3: The Pro Rata Plan

PRO RATA PLAN

Your plan should include as much prompt repayment of debt as possible, but YOU must set your priorities of repayment. Do NOT let a collector use your credit report as a _____ _____.

When you are unable to pay the minimum payments, use the _____ _____ plan.

WISDOM

"I've never been poor, only broke. Being poor is a frame of mind. Being broke is only a temporary position."

—Mike Todd

"A light purse is a heavy curse."

—Benjamin Franklin

PRO RATA DEBTS

"Pro rata" means the fair share, or the percent of your total debt each creditor represents. This will determine how much you should send them when you cannot make the minimum payments. Even if you cannot pay your creditors what they request, you should pay everyone as much as you can. Send the check for their pro rata share, along with a copy of your budget and this form, every month. Do this even if the creditor says they will not accept it.

Do you need to use the pro rata plan?

First, use your monthly cash flow plan to determine your total disposable income. Simply write down your income on the line at the top of the form. Then write down the total you spend on necessities (not including consumer debt) each month. Subtract the necessity expense from the income, and you are left with your disposable income. This is the money you have to put toward your debts.

Second, add up your total amount of debt, not including your home, and write that in the blank provided. Below that, write in the total of the minimum monthly payments on all your debts. If the total of your minimum payments is greater than your total disposable income, you need to use the pro rata plan.

How to Use This Form

This form has six columns:
1. Item: the name and type of the account.
2. Total Payoff: the total amount due on the account.
3. Total Debt: the combined total of all your debts.
4. Percent: the portion of the total debt load that each account represents. You can calculate this by simply dividing the Total Payoff by the Total Debt for each line.
5. Disposable Income: the amount of money you have left after paying necessities.
6. New Payment: the amount that you will now send to each creditor. Simply multiply the numbers in each line's Percent and Disposable Income columns for this figure.

The pro rata plan helps you to meet your obligations to the best of your ability. Your creditors will not like receiving less than their required minimum payments. However, if you keep sending them checks, they'll most likely keep cashing them.

Income _____ $336

Necessity Expense − _____ $316

Disposable Income = _____ $200

Total Debt: _____ $2,000

Total Minimum Payments: _____ $310

Item	Total Payoff	Total Debt	Percent	Disposable Income	New Payment
J.C. Penny	100	/ 2,000	= 5%(.05)	X 200	= $10
Sears	200	/ 2,000	= 10%(.10)	X 200	= $20
MBNA Visa	200	/ 2,000	= 10%(.10)	X 200	= $20
CitiBank Visa	100	/ 2,000	= 15%(.15)	X 200	= $30
Discover	1,200	/ 2,000	= 60%(.60)	X 200	= $120
	/	=	X	=
	/	=	X	=
	/	=	X	=
	/	=	X	=
	/	=	X	=
	/	=	X	=
	/	=	X	=
	/	=	X	=
	/	=	X	=
	/	=	X	=
	/	=	X	=
	/	=	X	=
	/	=	X	=
	/	=	X	=
	/	=	X	=

"Do not withhold good from those to whom it is due, when it is in the power of your hand to do it. Do not say to your neighbor, 'Go, and come back, and tomorrow I will give it,' when you have it with you."

—Old Testament

"Creditors have better memories than debtors."

—Benjamin Franklin

LAWSUITS

Eventually, if you are making no payments and have cut no deals, you will get sued.

Typically, lawsuits for under $_____ are filed in General Sessions Court (or small claims court), which is a fairly informal proceeding.

Before you are sued, you will be served by the local sheriff's department and typically given _____ days notice of the court date.

In court, if the debt is valid, even if you fight, you will _____. From that date, you will generally have 30 days before the _____ becomes final and garnishments or attachments begin.

At ANY TIME during the process, you may settle with the creditor or their attorney in writing. If you are not able to reach an agreement, you can file with the court a "_____ _____ motion," called a "pauper's oath" in some states.

Go online to take your quiz for *Credit Bureaus & Collections*!

FACTS YOU SHOULD KNOW

- Payment history on your credit file is supplied by credit grantors with whom you have credit. This includes both open accounts and accounts that have already been closed.

- Payment in full does not remove your payment history. The length of time information remains on file is:

  - Credit and collection accounts—Seven years from the date of last activity.

  - Courthouse records—Seven years from the date filed, except bankruptcy Chapters 7 and 11, which remain for 10 years from date filed.

- A divorce decree does not supersede the original contract with the creditor and does not release you from legal responsibility on any accounts. You must contact each creditor individually and seek their legally binding release of your obligation. Only after that release can your credit history be updated accordingly.

- There may appear to be duplicate accounts reported in your credit file. This could be because some credit grantors issue both revolving and installment accounts. Another reason is that when you move, some credit grantors transfer your account to a different location and issue another account number.

- The balance reported is the balance on the date the source reported the information. Credit grantors supply information on a periodic basis, so the balance shown may not be the balance you know it is today. If the balance reported was correct as of the date reported, it is not necessary to reinvestigate the balance on that account.

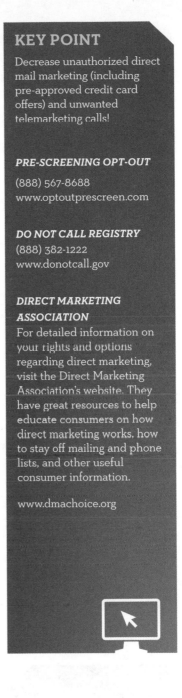

KEY POINT

Decrease unauthorized direct mail marketing (including pre-approved credit card offers) and unwanted telemarketing calls!

PRE-SCREENING OPT-OUT

(888) 567-8688
www.optoutprescreen.com

DO NOT CALL REGISTRY

(888) 382-1222
www.donotcall.gov

DIRECT MARKETING ASSOCIATION

For detailed information on your rights and options regarding direct marketing, visit the Direct Marketing Association's website. They have great resources to help educate consumers on how direct marketing works, how to stay off mailing and phone lists, and other useful consumer information.

www.dmachoice.org

CREDIT BUREAUS

The FACT Act amendments to the Fair Credit Reporting Act require the nationwide credit bureaus to provide consumers, upon request, one free personal credit report in any 12-month period. Contact the Central Source online at annualcreditreport.com or by calling toll free (877) FACT ACT. Free copies are also available if you have been denied credit in the past 60 days and the creditor used their services.

- EXPERIAN
  Phone: (888) 397-3742
  Website: www.experian.com

- EQUIFAX CREDIT BUREAU
  Phone: (800) 685-1111
  Website: www.equifax.com

- TRANSUNION CREDIT BUREAU
  Phone: (800) 888-4213
  Website: www.transunion.com

- FEDERAL TRADE COMMISSION
  Phone: (202) 326-2222
  Address: 600 Pennsylvania Avenue, N.W.
            Washington, D.C. 20580
  Website: www.ftc.gov

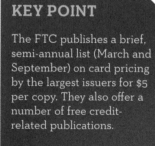

KEY POINT

The FTC publishes a brief, semi-annual list (March and September) on card pricing by the largest issuers for $5 per copy. They also offer a number of free credit-related publications.

SAMPLE LETTERS

Many people, especially in a high-pressure collection situation, fully remove themselves from the conversation and cut off all communication with their creditors. While you have the legal right to request that a collector stop contacting you (except to notify you of a lawsuit), we generally do not recommend stopping all contact. This action will often trigger a lawsuit that could have been avoided with simple, regular communication.

Instead, we recommend a regular schedule of talking to creditors once every two weeks. Tell them that you are willing and happy to talk to them that often, but you will not talk to them every day.

For written correspondence, we recommend sending actual letters through the mail using return receipt requested. That way, you will have physical proof that your letter was received. In the following pages, we have provided sample letters that you can adapt for your own use in specific situations.

REQUEST FOR FILE DISCLOSURE FORM

REQUEST FOR FILE DISCLOSURE

CREDIT BUREAU OF NASHVILLE

604 FOURTH AVE NORTH - P.O. BOX 190589 - NASHVILLE, TN 37219-0589

Reason for File Disclosure Request _____

Referred by _____ Was credit refused?   yes   no

I hereby request the Credit Bureau of Nashville to disclose to me the contents of my credit record. I understand that if I have been rejected for credit within the past sixty (60) days as the result of credit information contained in my credit record, there will be NO CHARGE for this disclosure, otherwise there will be an $8 charge for an individual disclosure or $10 for both myself and my spouse.

Name _____ Phone No. _____
Spouse's Name _____
Present Address _____
City _____ State _____ ZIP Code _____
Former Address _____
City _____ State _____ ZIP Code _____
Date of Birth _____ Social Security No. _____
Employed By _____
How Long? _____ Position _____
Former Employment _____
Spouse's Date of Birth _____Social Security No. _____

Spouse's Employment _____
How Long? _____ Position _____

I hereby authorize the Credit Bureau of Nashville to review my credit record with me, to make any necessary investigation of my credit transactions, and to furnish to its subscribers reports based thereon. In consideration of its undertaking to make such an investigation, I authorize any business or organization to give full information and records about me.

I am the person named above and I understand that federal law provides that a person who obtains information from a consumer reporting agency under false pretenses shall be fined not more than $5,000 or imprisoned no more than one year or both.

Signed _____ Date _____

Telephone Number _____ Ext. _____ where I can be reached during normal working hours.

AUTHORIZATION FOR DISCLOSURE OF SPOUSE'S CREDIT RECORD
I, _____, certify that I am presently married to _____ and am acting in his/her behalf in reviewing the credit record information concerning him/her maintained by the Credit Bureau of Nashville.

SAMPLE REMOVAL LETTER

Date _____

(From)

_____

_____

_____

VIA: Certified Mail, Return Receipt Requested

(To)

Mail Preference Service

Direct Marketing Association

P.O. Box 282

Carmel, NY 10512

RE: Unauthorized direct marketing and pre-approved credit card offers

This letter is your formal notice to remove my name from all direct marketing and pre-screening databases. I do not wish to receive any unsolicited offers, especially from credit card companies.

Not only do I request that my name be permanently removed, but I also request that my phone number and address must likewise be permanently removed. My correct information is as follows:

(Complete Name)
(Full Address)
(Phone Number with Area Code)

Thank you for your immediate attention to this matter.

Sincerely,

(Signatures)

SAMPLE CEASE AND DESIST LETTER

Date _____

(From)

_____

_____

_____

VIA: Certified Mail, Return Receipt Requested

(To)

_____

_____

_____

RE: _____

Dear _____,

You are hereby notified under provisions of Public Law 95-109, Section 805-C, the FAIR DEBT COLLECTION PRACTICES ACT to CEASE AND DESIST in any and all attempts to collect the above debt.

Your failure to do so WILL result in charges being filed against you with the state and federal regulatory agencies empowered with enforcement.

Please be further warned that if ANY derogatory information is placed on any credit reports after receipt of this notice, that too will result in action being taken against you.

PLEASE GIVE THIS MATTER YOUR IMMEDIATE ATTENTION.

Sincerely,

(Signature)

SAMPLE CREDIT BUREAU LETTER

Date _____

(From)

_____

_____

_____

(To)

_____

_____

_____

RE: _____

In reviewing the attached credit bureau report issued by your agency, I have detected an error. The following account(s) is/are reported inaccurately:

Company Name:_____
Account Number: _____

Under the provisions of the 1977 Federal Fair Credit Reporting Act, I hereby request that your agency prove to me in writing the accuracy of the reporting of this account. Under the terms of the Act and successive court cases, you have 30 days to prove such accuracy or remove the account entirely from my report. I ask that you do so.

This letter was sent certified mail, return receipt requested. I expect a response within the 30-day period. Should I not hear promptly from you, I will follow up with whatever action necessary to cause my report to be corrected.

Please feel free to call me if you have any questions. My home phone number is _____, and my office number is _____.

Sincerely,

(Signature)

SAMPLE CREDITOR LETTER

Date _____

(From)

_____

_____

_____

(To)

_____

_____

_____

RE: _____

Dear _____,

I am writing to formally request that, in accordance with the 1977 Federal Fair Debt Collection Practices Act, your firm (or any agency hired by your firm) no longer contact me at my place of employment, _____.

Please take note that this letter was mailed certified mail, return receipt requested, so that I will have proof that you are in receipt of this letter should legal action against you become necessary.

I am willing to pay the debt I owe you, and I will be in touch soon to work out arrangements.

Feel free to contact me at my home between _____ a.m. and _____ p.m. by phone at _____ or by mail at my home address:

_____

_____

Please give this matter your immediate attention.

Sincerely,

(Signature)

SAMPLE PRO RATA PLAN LETTER

Date: February 22, 2006

From: Joe and Suzie Public
        123 Anystreet
        Anytown, ST 11111

To: Mega Credit Card Company
        999 Main Street
        Big City, ST 00000

Re: Joe and Suzie Public # 1234-5678-9012-9999

Dear Collection Manager:

Recently I lost my job. My wife is employed in a clerical position. We have met with a financial counselor to assess our present situation.

We acknowledge our indebtedness to you of $6,000 and fully intend to pay you back in full. However, you are one of six creditors to whom we owe a total of $42,968. We owe minimum payments of $782 each month. We are not able to meet these minimum payments at the present time, and we will not go further into debt to meet these obligations.

We have put together a cash flow plan based on our take-home pay of $2,340 per month (see the enclosed copy of cash flow plan). Since we have two small children and no disposable income, we cannot make a payment to you at the present time, but we do not intend to go bankrupt.

We are asking for a moratorium on payments for the next 120 days. We will keep in close contact with you, and we will begin making payments as soon as we are able. If possible, we further request a reduction in interest during this time.

We are aware that this is an inconvenience to you, but we must meet the basic needs of our family first. We fully intend to pay our creditors all that we owe them. Please be patient with us. If you have any questions please contact us at 600-555-9876.

Thank you for your consideration of our present situation.

Sincerely,

(Signature)

NEXT STEPS

Something get your attention in this lesson? Write it down!

ANSWER KEY

Credit	Complaints
Score	Plan
Debt	Money
Winning	Salespeople
7	Telemarketers
10	Turnover
Inaccurate	Emotion
79	Necessities
25	You
30	8:00 a.m.
22	9:00 p.m.
Annually	Work
Fraud Victim	All
Police Report	Lawsuit
Theft	Negotiations
Nothing	Take
Nothing	Wages
Division	Paper Club
Documentation	Pro Rata
Persistent	10,000
Hobby	10
Remove	Lose
Certified	Judgment
Entire	Slow Pay

KEY POINTS

1. The FICO score is not a measure of wealth. It is an "I Love Debt" score, based only on debt.

2. Under the Federal Fair Debt Collections Practices Act, you have specific legal protections from abusive, out-of-control collectors.

3. If you are unable to pay the minimum payments on your debts, use the pro rata plan.

4. You should check your credit report for errors at least once a year, which you can do for free.

QUESTIONS FOR REFLECTION

1. How has your understanding of the FICO score changed since viewing this lesson?

2. What is a collector's one and only job?

3. In what way is emotion a collector's best weapon?

_____

_____

4. How might a collector try to set your family's priorities? What could you say in response to such tactics?

_____

_____

5. What are the "Four Walls"? Why is it important to always pay necessities first before paying your creditors such as credit card companies?

_____

_____

6. How would identity theft impact your life? What precautions can you take to protect yourself?

_____

_____

PERSONAL APPLICATION

After viewing *Credit Bureaus & Collections*, be sure to complete these action items before moving on to the next lesson.

- Review your credit report. You can get a free copy from each of the three credit agencies once a year. Check it for accuracy immediately!

- To remove your name and phone number from telemarketing call lists, visit the National Do Not Call Registry's website, www.donotcall.gov.

THE *impact* of MARKETING

LET THE BUYER BEWARE

Can you recite, from memory, the advertising slogans of at least 10 companies? Have you ever experienced "buyer's remorse"? America is the most marketed-to country on Earth. Thousands of companies are clamoring for our money—and we usually run to hand it to them!

In *The Impact of Marketing*, Dave draws on years of selling and marketing experience to show you exactly how all of these businesses get their message deep into your subconscious, without you even realizing it. Then, once you understand the game, Dave will give you five keys to (finally) gaining power over your purchases!

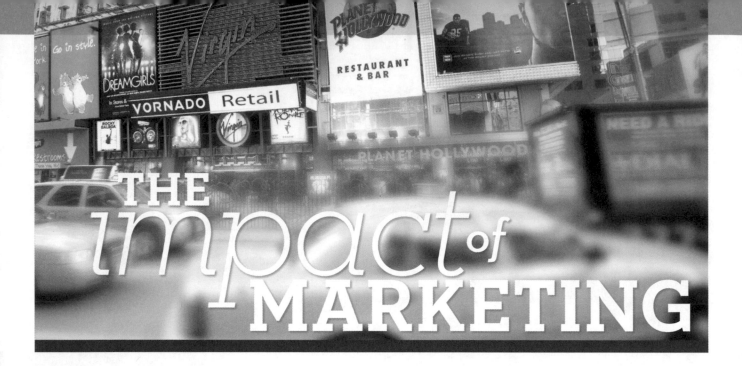

THE *impact* of MARKETING

▶ **Video 1:** Learn Their Game

CAVEAT EMPTOR
(LET THE BUYER BEWARE)

Profile of the Enemy
(The enemy of your Financial Peace)

Companies use every angle to aggressively compete for your _____.

FOUR MAJOR WAYS

1. _____ selling

2. _____ as a marketing tool
   _____% of 90-days-same-as-cash contracts convert to payments, which are usually at _____% APR with Rule of 78s prepayment penalty.

3. _____, _____, _____ and other media

4. Product _____
   - Brand Recognition
   - Shelf Position
   - Color
   - Packaging

SIGNIFICANT PURCHASES

A "significant purchase" is normally anything over
$_____. Our bodies go through physiological
_____ when making a significant purchase.

We all have that spoiled, red-faced, grocery store kid
living inside of us. His name is _____.

WHAT TO DO

Because you can always spend more than you _____,
you must develop a power over _____ by:

1. Waiting _____ before making a purchase.

2. Carefully considering your buying _____.

3. Understanding no amount of _____ equals
   contentment or fulfillment.

4. Never buying anything you do not _____.

5. Considering the "_____ _____"
   of your money.

6. Seeking the _____ of your spouse.

Go online to take your quiz for *The Impact of Marketing*!

WISDOM

"Almost any man knows how to make money, but not one in a million knows how to spend it."

—Henry David Thoreau

"For where your treasure is, there your heart will be also."

—New Testament

"It is the mark of an educated mind to be able to entertain a thought without accepting it."

—Aristotle

NEXT STEPS

Something get your attention in this lesson? Write it down!

_____

_____

_____

_____

_____

ANSWER KEY

Money	Immaturity
Personal	Make
Financing	Purchase
88	Overnight
24	Motives
TV	Stuff
Radio	Understand
Internet	Opportunity
Positioning	Cost
300	Counsel
Changes	

KEY POINTS

1. Marketing companies use specific, easily recognized techniques to encourage you to buy. By learning their methods, you can take control of every purchase.

2. Never make a major purchase (above $300) without first waiting overnight.

3. If married, always talk to your spouse before making a major purchase.

QUESTIONS FOR REFLECTION

1. How do marketers use emotion to compel you to purchase their goods?

   _____

   _____

2. How can waiting overnight before making a purchase change your behavior?

   _____

   _____

3. How would you define a "major purchase"? Why is it so important for married couples to agree on major purchases?

_____

_____

4. What can singles do to guard themselves against impulsive buying decisions?

_____

_____

5. How can you ensure that you will genuinely enjoy your purchases?

_____

_____

6. Has an accountability partner been helpful to you?

_____

_____

PERSONAL APPLICATION

After viewing *The Impact of Marketing*, be sure to complete these action items before moving on to the next lesson.

- Memorize the five keys to gaining power over your purchases, and make yourself accountable to someone for following these principles for every major purchase.

- Learn your rights when it comes to marketing databases, direct mail (junk mail) and annoying telemarketing calls. Go to dmachoice.org for more information.

THE *power* of NEGOTIATING

THAT'S NOT GOOD ENOUGH!

Have you ever haggled over a price at a retail electronics store? When was the last time you asked for a deep discount at the department store? The average consumer would never dream of "embarrassing" himself like this. That's crazy! We're handing these people our money hand over fist, and yet we are reluctant to demand a good deal! Why would we do this?

In *The Power of Negotiating*, Dave reveals the keys to a true "win-win" negotiation and teaches you how, when and where to find amazing deals on the products and services you use every day!

THE power of NEGOTIATING

▶ Video 1: Creating A Win-Win Deal

KEY POINT

You cannot have healthy relationships and build wealth with lies as your foundation.

GROUND RULES FOR BIG BARGAINS

It is proper to get a great deal if you:

1. Have in no way _____ the truth.

2. Have not set out to _____ the other party.

3. Have created a _____ - _____ deal.

THE FIRST KEY

WISDOM

"Nothing astonishes men so much as common sense and plain dealing."

—Ralph Waldo Emerson

The first key to opening the door to huge bargains is learning to _____ everything.

Win-win deals really work, so don't be _____ to _____ for the deal!

▶ Video 2: The Number-One Rule of Negotiating

LUCKY SEVEN BASIC RULES OF NEGOTIATING

1. Always tell the absolute _____.

▶ Video 3: The Other Six Rules Of Negotiating

2. Use the power of _____.

   ▪ Cash is _____.

   ▪ Cash is _____.

   ▪ Cash has _____.

3. Understand and use "_____ _____ power."

4. _____ _____.

5. "That's not _____ _____!"

6. _____ guy, _____ guy.

7. The "If I _____ _____" technique.

▶ Video 4: Finding Deals: Waiting and Watching

THE SECOND KEY

The second key to opening the door to huge bargains is that you must have _____.

Don't get _____ to a purchase.

THE THIRD KEY

The third key to opening the door to huge bargains is that you must know _____ to _____ deals.

_____ something of value, goods or just your _____.

PLACES TO FIND GREAT DEALS

1. _____
2. Estate Sales
3. _____ _____
4. Couponing
5. _____ _____
6. Repo Lot
7. _____ _____

8. Refunding
9. _____
10. Pawn Shops
11. _____ _____
12. Classified Ads
13. _____
      _____
14. Conventions

Go online to take your quiz for *The Power of Negotiating!*

WHAT WAS YOUR BEST DEAL ...

How did other class members answer the question, "What's your best 'Big Bargain' deal ever?"

New refrigerator. Samsung® side-by-side, freezer on the bottom. They had last year's model in the back as an open box. Regular retail was $1,800; I paid $900! —*Shelley*

$500 off a Tempurpedic® mattress—which they say they NEVER discount! —*Susie*

Living room sectional marked down from $1,599 to $598 on Black Friday weekend. Man, it feels good to pay cash! —*Markie*

MacBook Pro® at a big box store. Hubby just kept telling them the price wasn't good enough and used walkaway power. Got a brand-new model at a discount, earned store rewards, and got a few extras thrown in. Oh, and we paid in CASH! —*Jen*

$80 worth of groceries for $20! With groceries being an ongoing expense, our savings each week are equivalent to over $1,000 at the end of the year! —*Beth*

Baby formula on Ebay®. Saved $200 by buying four cases. I checked expiration dates before ordering, and they are good through 2013. LOVE IT! Also, I bought baby wipes online and got them for three cents each versus five cents in the store. I bought a case of 796 wipes and saved $15.94! —*Angie*

$589 water heater for $250 via Craigslist® from an installer that buys returns from Home Depot®. Also, we're now saving on utility costs with a more efficient heater! —*Jeff*

I follow some coupon blogs and got $113.05 in groceries at Winn-Dixie® for $37.16 and $59.24 in groceries at Publix® for $16.39! —*Kris*

... EVER?

NEXT STEPS

Something get your attention in this lesson? Write it down!

ANSWER KEY

Misrepresented	Take Away
Harm	Patience
Win Win	Married
Negotiate	Where
Afraid	Find
Ask	Trade
Truth	Services
Cash	Individuals
Emotional	Public
Visual	Auctions
Immediacy	Garage Sales
Walk Away	Flea Markets
Shut Up	Foreclosures
Good Enough	Online
Good	Auctions
Bad	Consignment
	Sales

KEY POINTS

1. Do not be afraid to negotiate when making a purchase, and always be willing to walk away if the deal isn't right.

2. Always use the power of cash when making a purchase anywhere, anytime.

3. Do not assume that "sale" means "deal." Find the places in your area where you can get genuine deals and shop there as much as possible.

QUESTIONS FOR REFLECTION

1. Why do most people avoid negotiating for deals?

_____

_____

2. Describe a time when you found a great bargain. Was it a win-win?

_____

_____

3. Why is integrity so important in the area of bargain hunting?

_____

_____

4. How often do you actually ask for a deal when shopping? If you don't do it often, what's stopping you?

_____

_____

5. Are you plagued by impulse purchases? What goes through your heart and mind when you are tempted to spend?

_____

_____

6. How does an envelope system change impulse buying decisions? Has this worked for you?

_____

_____

PERSONAL APPLICATION

After viewing *The Power of Negotiating*, be sure to complete these action items before moving on to the next lesson.

- Memorize the seven rules of negotiating and begin using them in all sales interactions.

- Can you recite all Baby Steps in order? If not, revisit the list and commit all seven to memory.

long-term *career* **PLANNING**

WORKING IN YOUR STRENGTHS

"Thank God, it's Friday! Oh God, it's Monday!" Does this characterize your attitude about work? Do you live for the weekend and start dreading Monday morning by lunch on Sunday? Sadly, a LOT of people feel this way about their jobs, but you don't have to!

In *Long-Term Career Planning*, Dave shows you how vital it is to love what you do for a living. If you aren't doing what you love, it may be time for a change. That doesn't necessarily mean leaving your company, however! It's all about finding the right seat on the bus so you can truly thrive by working in your strengths.

long-term Career PLANNING

▶ **Video 1:** Getting to Know Yourself

CHANGE HAPPENS

The average job is now only ___2.1___ years in length.

This means that the average worker could have as many as ___20___ different jobs in his or her working lifetime.

Small business is changing the way we think about work. ___98.3___% of the companies in America have fewer than 100 employees.

WISDOM

"Commit your works to the LORD, and your thoughts will be established."

—Old Testament

"To find out what one is fitted to do, and to secure an opportunity to do it, is the key to happiness."

—John Dewey

DISCOVER YOUR STRENGTHS AND WEAKNESSES

How can you know ___Where___ you ought to be and ___What___ you ought to be doing if you don't know ___Who___ you are?

Speaker and author Marcus Buckingham has identified some common myths that often rob people of having fulfillment and enjoyment in their careers.

 As you grow, you ___Change___.

 You do not ___Outgrow___ **your personality.**

. . . .

MYTH You will learn and grow the most in the areas in which you are ___Weakest___.

TRUTH You grow in your ___Strengths___. You will grow the most in the areas that you already know and love the most.

"The master in the art of living makes little distinction between his work and his play, his labor and his leisure, his mind and his body, his information and his recreation, his love and his religion.

He hardly knows which is which. He simply pursues his vision of excellence at whatever he does, leaving others to decide whether he is working or playing. To him, he is always doing both."

—James Michener

"Everything that irritates us about others can lead us to an understanding of ourselves."

—Carl Jung

IDENTIFY YOUR MOTIVATION AND PASSION

Career coach Dan Miller reminds us that __Money__ is ultimately never enough compensation for doing a job.

Find something that blends your skills, __Abilities__, personality traits, __Values__, dreams and __Passions__.

UNDERSTAND YOUR UNIQUE PERSONALITY

The __DISC__ profile is a simple exercise that will yield tremendous insight into how you process decisions and what your natural tendencies may be.

- The D (__Dominant__) person is a hard-charging driver that is task-oriented and first looks to __Problems__.

- The I (__Influencing__) person is people-oriented, fun, outgoing and generally concerned about people-pleasing, so they first look to __People__.

- The S (__Stable__) person is amiable, loyal, does not like conflict and is concerned about __Pace__.

- The C (__Compliant__) person is analytical, loves detail, factual, can seem rigid and loves __Procedures__.

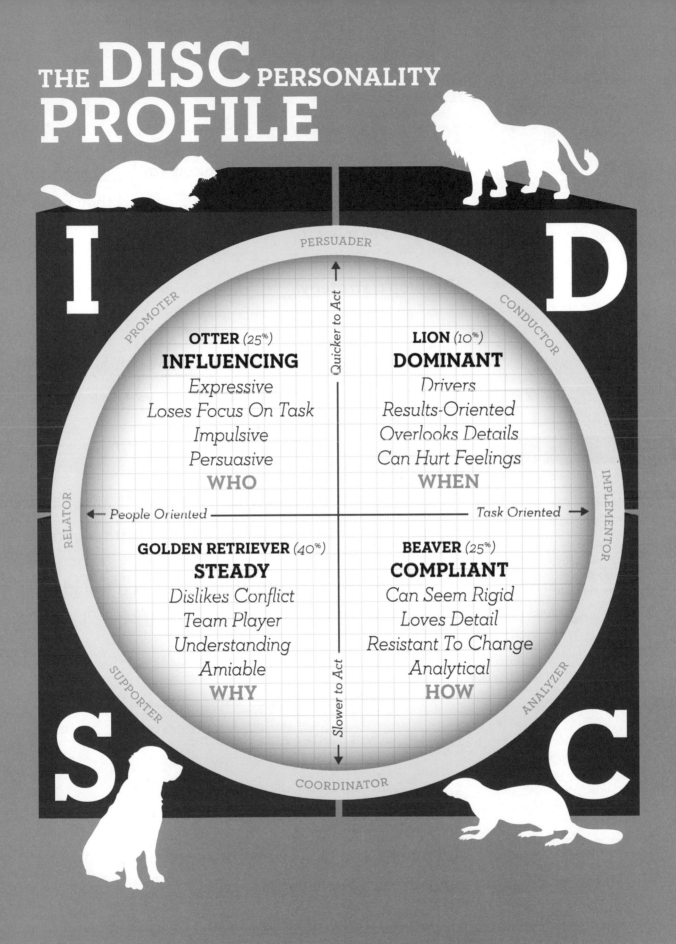

JOB HUNTING

Companies do not start out looking for ___You___.

They have a specific ___Need___, and they need someone to meet it.

Develop a strategy:

- Identify your ___Target___.

- ___Learn___ everything you can about them.

RÉSUMÉS

When it is time to contact the company, think of it like starting a new ___Relationship___ with a person.

After you target the companies where you would most like to work, you are going to contact them at least three times.

- Introduction ___Letter___

- Cover Letter and Résumé

- ___Phone___ Follow-up

Interviews and jobs come from persistent follow-up and ___Networking___.

INTERVIEWS

Present yourself well. You are the ___Product___, so make it the best one available.

Be on ___Time___, address everyone by ___Name___, offer a firm, confident ___Handshake___, and maintain ___Eye___ contact at all times.

Designate a time to ___Follow___ ___Up___ after the interview ... and DO IT!

▶ **Video 3:** Overtime and Extra Jobs

OVERTIME AND EXTRA JOBS

Raising your income ___Long___-term is a career-track issue. Raising it ___Short___-term means the dreaded part-time job.

HOW DO YOU GET STARTED WITH AN EXTRA JOB?

- Be willing to ___Sacrifice___ to win.
- Have a detailed ___Plan___ so you can see the finish line. This gives you hope!
- Choose the ___Job___ or start a ___Home___-___Based___ business.
- Don't ___Give___ ___Up___!

Beware! Do not allow your work to be the source of all your satisfaction and self-___Worth___.

🔲 Go online to take your quiz for *Long-Term Career Planning*!

HOME-BASED BUSINESS IDEAS

Accounting
Auditing
Bookkeeping
Columnist
Computer Technician
Copywriter
Customer Service
Data Entry Clerk
Editor
Fundraiser
Graphic Artist
Information Specialist
LAN Manager
Lawyer
Market Researcher
Online Auctions
Probation Officer
Programmer
Public Relations
Real Estate Agent
Records Manager
Reporter
Researcher
Sales Representative
Systems Analyst
Technical Writer
Telemarketer
Transcriber
Translator
Travel Agent
Web Design

Part-Time Job Ideas:
Car Detailing
Carpentry
Handyman
Maid Service
Newspaper Delivery
Pizza Delivery
Waiter
Yard Work

NEXT STEPS

Something get your attention in this lesson? Write it down!

ANSWER KEY

2.1	You
20	Need
98.3	Target
Where	Learn
What	Relationship
Who	Letter
Change	Phone
Outgrow	Networking
Weakest	Product
Strengths	Time
Money	Name
Abilities	Handshake
Values	Eye
Passions	Follow
DISC	Up
Dominant	Long
Problems	Short
Influencing	Sacrifice
People	Plan
Stable	Job
Pace	Home Based
Compliant	Give Up
Procedures	Worth

KEY POINTS

1. The age of retiring from one company after 35 years is over. The average job in America now lasts just over two years.

2. The key to career success is to first look at yourself. You can't know what you really want to do if you don't first understand who you really are.

3. Plan your work around your life; don't plan your life around your work. You are more than what you do for a living.

QUESTIONS FOR REFLECTION

1. What areas of growth or education will help you along your career path?

   _____
   _____

2. Based on your unique personality, what strengths do you bring to the workplace?

   _____
   _____

3. Have you spent time focusing on your weakest areas? Was that beneficial, or was it simply draining and discouraging?

_____

_____

4. Talk about the danger of being a workaholic. How can it affect your life, spirit and family? Is this a non-issue if you are single?

_____

_____

5. Have you tried any creative home-based business ideas?

_____

_____

PERSONAL APPLICATION

After viewing *Long-Term Career Planning*, be sure to complete these action items before moving on to the next lesson.

- Review the DISC chart in your workbook to determine if your current line of work naturally fits within your unique personality style.

- Lay out a three-year professional plan in which you envision exactly what you want to be doing three years from now, either within your current organization or elsewhere. Then, identify the steps to get there.

- Leaders are readers. The average millionaire reads one nonfiction book every month. If you haven't read one lately, set a goal to read one this month.

THE Power OF GIVING

UNLEASHING THE POWER OF GENEROUS GIVING

Why is it so important to get control over our money? Dave says that there are only three things we can do with money: SPEND it (we've got that one down!), INVEST it (we're learning!), and GIVE it. What? How can we build wealth if we're constantly giving our money away? That's what Dave calls "The Great Misunderstanding," and it can change your life.

In *The Power of Giving* bonus lesson, Dave discusses the commonly held misperceptions many people have about giving and reveals the true key to winning—both with your life and your money.

THE Power OF GIVING

▶ **Video 1:** Instructions for Giving

WISDOM

"You can't shake hands with a clenched fist."

—Golda Meir

"There are men who gain from their wealth only the fear of losing it."

—Antoine Rivaroli

"Surplus wealth is a sacred trust to be managed for the good of others."

—Andrew Carnegie

BABY STEP 7

Build wealth and _____!

You can do everything we teach and you will prosper, but if you don't understand this lesson, you will never have _____ _____.

"The Great Misunderstanding," the paradox, is the mistaken belief that the way to have _____ is to hold on _____.

OWNERS AND MANAGERS

We are asset _____ for the _____, so if we view it properly, we aren't giving our own money anyway.

A _____ is a manager, not an _____.

Why does God tell us to _____ so often?

Giving makes us more _____-like;
a spiritually mature Christian gives.

Giving moves you to become less _____,
and less selfish people have more of a tendency to
_____ in relationships and in wealth.

Because we are designed in God's image, we are happiest and most fulfilled when _____ and _____.

WHY GIVE?

Giving is:

1. A _____ of _____
2. _____ and _____
3. _____   _____

INSTRUCTIONS FOR GIVING

"When you have finished paying all the tithe of your increase ..."

—Old Testament

"This stone, which I have set up as a pillar, will be God's house, and of all that you give me I will surely give a tenth to you."

—Old Testament

"Woe to you, teachers of the law and Pharisees, you hypocrites! You give a tenth of your spices—mint, dill and cumin. But you have neglected the more important matters of the law—justice, mercy and faithfulness. You should have practiced the latter, without neglecting the former."

—New Testament

The tithe is a tenth (10%) of your _____.

The Bible says to give first fruits, meaning off the _____.

The tithe is to go to your _____ _____, which provides the same function as the Old Testament _____.

_____ are different than the tithe. They are _____ the tithe and are freely given from _____.

The tithe is _____.

The tithe is _____ _____.

Never give with the _____ of having your giving _____.

"Financial Peace" is more than just God's system for understanding money, becoming debt-free, and building wealth.

"Financial Peace" is when The Great Misunderstanding is _____.

Go online to take your quiz for *The Power of Giving!*

GIVING & RECEIVING

How did other class members answer the question, "What's your best giving story?"

When my son was terminally ill, a group of coworkers volunteered to get sponsors and run a 5K to raise money on our behalf. I didn't think much of it, except for the fact that it was an incredible gesture of compassion and caring that I greatly appreciated. A month after the 5K, they handed me an envelope. The checks and cash totaled over $6,000. I couldn't believe it! I was so overwhelmed, I busted out in tears.

I was told that the reason it took so long to get me the money was that one of the folks had asked his entire family back in India to chip in, and it took that long to get all the checks to the U.S. from there. His fundraising alone was over half of the total.

There are good people out there, and God places them in our lives when we need them the most. —*Terry*

When I got on a budget, I was finally able to start giving, and I sponsored a child through Compassion International. I am now sponsoring two children, and I became a local advocate with Compassion, so I've been able to facilitate the sponsorship of many more children. None of that would have been possible if I hadn't started the Baby Steps! —*Melissa*

I can reach in my pocket and give at any time without questioning whether or not bills will get paid! —*Dani*

I knew a single mom who was struggling. I bought a whole pile of $25 gift cards to different stores and anonymously mailed one per week to her for about six months. I heard her tell someone else that it wasn't the money that helped so much as having something to look forward to each week. The anticipation gave her hope and excitement, which helped ease the day-to-day struggles she was having. —*Cher*

I was waiting to board a plane with my three small children, and another woman overheard me chatting to someone about my deployed spouse. She came over and handed me a $50 bill, saying, "Dinner's on me. Thank you so much for your service." I told her at first that I couldn't accept her gift, but she said, "Oh yes you can!" My reply: "Yes ma'am! And thanks!" —*Cris*

BABY STEPS

Here's a review of the Baby Step covered in this lesson:

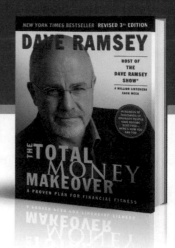

Build wealth and give!
For more insight, see Chapters 12 and 13 of
The Total Money Makeover.

ANSWER KEY

Give	Praise
Financial	Worship
Peace	Spiritual
More	Warfare
Tightly	Increase
Managers	Top
Lord	Local
Steward	Church
Owner	Storehouse
Give	Offerings
Christ	Above
Selfish	Surplus
Prosper	Pre-law
Serving	New Testament
Giving	Motive
Reminder	Returned
Ownership	Understood

KEY POINTS

1. "The Great Misunderstanding"—the paradox—is that we believe the way to have more is to hold on more tightly to what we already have.

2. A steward is a manager, not an owner.

3. Giving is a key part to overall success. Give the first 10% of your income to your church or favorite charity.

QUESTIONS FOR REFLECTION

1. Why don't we give as much as we'd like to at times?

   _____

   _____

2. How do you feel when you give?

   _____

   _____

3. Has anyone ever surprised you with a meaningful act of giving? How did that make you feel?

   _____

   _____

4. Why is it important to give while paying off debts?

_____

_____

5. How does viewing yourself as a manager of God's resources affect your thinking and behavior about money?

_____

_____

6. What's the most important lesson you've learned in CORE *Financial Wellness*?

_____

_____

7. In what ways has your life changed as a result of getting your money under control?

_____

_____

PERSONAL APPLICATION

After viewing *The Power of Giving*, be sure to complete these action items.

- Identify some specific ways to give, whether to a church, ministry, nonprofit or other charity. If giving is not a consistent line item in your monthly budget, make that change today!

- Optional: Read Chapters 12 and 13 of *The Total Money Makeover*.

APPENDIX
GLOSSARY

401(k): defined contribution plan offered by a corporation to its employees, which allows employees to set aside tax-deferred income for retirement purposes; in some cases, employers will match their contributions.

403(b): retirement plan similar to a 401(k) plan, but one that is offered by nonprofit organizations, such as universities and some charitable organizations, rather than corporations; employees set aside tax-deferred dollars.

457 plan: non-qualified, deferred compensation plan established by state and local governments for tax-exempt government agencies and tax-exempt employers; eligible employees are allowed to make salary deferral contributions to the 457 plan; earnings grow on a tax-deferred basis and contributions are not taxed until the assets are distributed from the plan.

501(c)(3): An incorporated, tax-exempt, charitable organization as defined in the United States tax code, section 501(c)(3), that encompasses the general legal definition as a "charitable" organization. A 501(c)(3) status is granted to an organization by the United States Internal Revenue Service (IRS). Section 501(c) of the tax code also outlines other tax-exempt organization of various purposes.

529 plan: college savings plan that allows individuals to save on a tax-deferred basis in order to fund future college and graduate school expenses of a child or beneficiary; generally sponsored by a state, these are professionally managed investments.

Adjustable Rate Mortgage (ARM): home loan secured by a deed of trust or mortgage in which the interest rate will change periodically (i.e. annually); typically adjusted based on a published index such as the Treasury Bill or LIBOR; brought on as a result of high interest rates in the early 1980s as a way for banks to transfer the risk of higher interest rates to the consumer.

Aggressive Growth Stock Mutual Fund: mutual fund that seeks to provide maximum long-term capital growth from stocks of primarily smaller companies or narrow market segments; dividend income is incidental; the most volatile fund; also referred to as a small-cap fund.

Amortization Table: breakdown showing how much of each regular payment will be applied toward principal and how much toward interest over the life of a loan; also shows the gradual decrease of the loan balance until it reaches zero.

Annuity: contract sold by an insurance company, designed to provide payments to the holder at specified intervals, usually after retirement; the holder is taxed at the time of distribution or withdrawal, making this a tax-deferred arrangement.

Annual Percentage Rate (APR): cost of borrowing money on an annual basis; takes into account the interest rate and other related fees on a loan.

Asset: anything that is owned by an individual; with respect to saving and investing, assets are generally categorized as liquid (cash) and capital (investment) assets.

Back-End Load: sales commission paid when the investor sells mutual fund shares; sometimes phased out over several years; also called redemption fee or contingent-deferred sales charge.

Balanced Fund: mutual fund that invests in more than one type of financial asset: stocks, bonds, and in some cases, cash investments.

Balloon Mortgage: home loan in which the sum of the monthly payments is insufficient to repay the entire loan; a final payment comes due, which is a lump sum of the remaining principal balance.

Bankruptcy: legal procedure for dealing with debt problems of individuals and businesses; specifically, a legal court case filed under one of the chapters of Title 11 of the United States Code (also see Chapter 7 bankruptcy, Chapter 11 bankruptcy, and Chapter 13 bankruptcy).

Bond: debt instrument where an issuer such as a corporation, municipality, or government agency owes you money; a form of I.O.U.; the issuer makes regular interest payments on the bond and promises to pay back or redeem the face value of the bond at a specified point in the future (the maturity date).

Break-Even Analysis: method used to evaluate the wisdom of a financial decision by determining the length of time it will take for cost of the decision to be recouped.

Budget: cash flow plan; assigns every dollar to a specific category/expense the beginning of each month.

Cash Value Insurance: also known as permanent life insurance; premiums include a death benefit and plan to build savings within the policy; two main types are whole life and universal life; significantly more expensive than term life insurance.

C.D.: Certificate of Deposit, usually at a bank; savings account with a slightly higher interest rate because of a longer savings commitment (i.e. six months, one year, etc.).

Chapter 7 Bankruptcy: chapter of the Bankruptcy Code providing for liquidation of the debtor's assets in order to repay the creditors; certain assets or aggregate value of assets of the debtor may be exempt based on state law.

Chapter 11 Bankruptcy: reorganization bankruptcy, usually involving a corporation or partnership; generally includes a plan of reorganization to keep a business alive and pay creditors over time.

Chapter 13 Bankruptcy: chapter of the Bankruptcy Code providing for an individual to repay debts over time, usually three to five years; debtor makes periodic payments to the bankruptcy trustee, who in turn pays the creditors; sometimes includes adjustments to debt balances within the bankruptcy.

Check Card: type of card, often bearing the seal of a major credit card company, issued by a bank and used to make purchases; unlike a credit card, the money comes directly out of a checking account; also called debit card.

Collision: portion of auto insurance that covers losses due to vehicle damage in an accident.

Compound Interest: interest paid on interest previously earned; credited daily, monthly, quarterly, semi-annually, or annually on both principal and previously credited interest.

Contents Policy: insurance policy that covers your possessions in a home or apartment; sometimes called "renter's insurance."

Conventional Loan: mortgage obtained through the Federal National Mortgage Association (FNMA), which insures against default; generally includes a down payment of 5-20% or more.

Cosigning: offering to guarantee someone else's loan; responsible for loan repayment if the borrower defaults.

Credit Laws:

- **Fair Credit Reporting Act (1971):** federal law governing the reporting of debt repayment information; establishes when a credit reporting agency may provide a report to someone; states that obsolete information must be taken off (seven to 10 years); gives consumers the right to know what is in their credit report; requires that both a credit bureau and information provider (i.e. department store) have an obligation to correct wrong information; gives consumers the right to dispute inaccurate information and add a 100-word statement to their report to explain accurate negative information; gives consumers the right to know what credit bureau provided the report when they are turned down for credit.

- **Fair Credit Billing Act (1975):** federal law that covers credit card billing problems and applies to all open-end credit accounts (i.e. credit cards and overdraft checking); states that consumers should send a written billing error notice to the creditor within 60 days (after receipt of first bill containing an error), which the creditor must acknowledge in 30 days; requires the creditor to investigate and prohibits them from damaging a consumer's credit rating while a dispute is pending.

- **Fair Debt Collection Practices Act (1978):** federal law that prohibits debt collectors from engaging in unfair, deceptive, or abusive practices when collecting debts; requires collectors to send a written notice stating the name of the creditor and the amount owed; prohibits contacting the consumer if he or she disputes in writing within 30 days (unless collector furnishes proof of the debt); requires collectors to identify themselves on the phone and limits calls to between 8:00 a.m. and 9:00 p.m. unless the consumer agrees to another time; prohibits calling the consumer at work if requested.

- **Equal Credit Opportunity Act (1975):** federal law that ensures consumers are given an equal chance to receive credit; prohibits discrimination on the basis of gender, race, marital status, religion, national origin, age, or receipt of public assistance; prohibits lenders from asking about plans to have children or refusing to consider consistently received alimony or child support payments as income; grants the consumer legal rights to know why he or she was denied credit.

- **Truth in Lending Act (1969):** federal law that mandates disclosure of information about the cost of credit; mandates that the finance charge (i.e. all charges to borrow money, including interest) and the annual percentage rate (APR) must be displayed prominently on forms and statements used by creditors; provides criminal penalties for willful violators, as well as civil remedies; protects against unauthorized use of one's credit card, limiting personal loss to $50 if the card is lost or stolen.

- **Fair Credit and Charge Card Disclosure Act (1989):** portion of the Truth in Lending Act that mandates a section on credit card applications that describes key features and cost (i.e. APR, grace period for purchases, minimum finance charge, balance calculation method, annual fees, transaction fees for cash advances, and penalty fees such as over-the-limit fees and late payment fees).

Debit Card: see Check Card.

Debt Consolidation: act of combining all debts into one monthly payment, typically extending the terms and the length of time required to repay the debt.

Debt Snowball: preferred method of debt repayment; includes a list of all debts organized from smallest to largest balance; minimum payments are made to all debts except for the smallest, which is attacked with the largest possible payments.

Deductible: amount you have to pay out-of-pocket for expenses before the insurance company will begin contributing to cover all or a portion of the remaining costs.

Direct Transfer: movement of tax-deferred retirement plan money from one qualified plan or custodian to another; results in no immediate tax liabilities or penalties, but requires IRS reporting.

Disability Insurance: policy that insures a worker in the event of an occupational mishap resulting in disability; compensates the injured worker for lost pay.

Diversification: to spread around one's investment dollars among several different classes of financial assets and among the securities of many issuers; results in lowered risk.

Dividend: distribution of a portion of a company's earnings, decided by the board of directors, to a class of its shareholders; generally distributed in the form of cash or stock.

Educational Savings Account (ESA): after-tax college fund that grows tax-free for educational uses; eligibility based on parents' annual income.

Elimination Period: amount of time that lapses after a disabling event and before the insurance company begins to pay benefits.

Emergency Fund: three to six months of expenses in readily available cash to be used only in the event of an emergency; Baby Step 3.

Envelope System: series of envelopes, divided into pre-determined categories, used to store cash for planned monthly expenses; self-imposed discipline tool to assist people in managing their monthly finances; possible categories include food, entertainment, gas, etc.

Equity: one's stake, or level of ownership, in an item of value.

Fixed Annuity: type of annuity that guarantees a certain rate of return; see annuity.

Forbearance: agreement between a lender and a debtor to "catch up" a past due account over a specified period of time; lender grants a postponement of loan payments for a set period of time, giving the borrower time to make up for overdue payments.

Foreclosure: process by which the holder of a mortgage seizes the property of a homeowner who has not made interest and/or principal payments on time as stipulated in the mortgage contract.

For Profit Corporation: An incorporated organization that is established or designed to make a profit. Profit is distributed to the shareholders and owners of the company.

Front-End Load: sales commission that is paid up-front when shares of a mutual fund are purchased.

Garnishment: court-ordered settlement that allows a lender to take monies owed directly from a borrower's paycheck; only allowed as part of a court judgment.

Grace Period: time period during which a borrower can pay the full balance of credit due with no finance charges.

Growth and Income Mutual Fund: funds that buy stocks in larger, more established companies; contain medium-sized companies or growth stocks; also called a large-cap fund.

Growth Stock Mutual Fund: funds that buy stock in medium-sized companies that have experienced some growth and are still expanding; also called a mid-cap fund.

Home Equity Loan (HEL): credit line offered by mortgage lenders that allows a homeowner to borrow money against the equity in their home.

Homeowner's Insurance: policy that covers a loss due to damage, theft, or injury within one's home.

House Poor: condition of having a disproportionately high house payment that limits one's ability to maintain the home and/or meet necessities.

Individual Retirement Account/Arrangement (IRA): tax-deferred arrangement for individuals with earned income and their non-income-producing spouses; growth is not taxed until money is withdrawn; contributions to an IRA are often tax-deductible.

Inflation: rate at which the general level of prices for goods and services rises.

Interest: 1) charge for borrowed money generally defined as a percentage. 2) money paid to savers and investors by financial institutions, governments, or corporations for the use of their money (such as a 2% return on money held in a savings account).

Interest Rate: percentage paid to a lender for the use of borrowed money.

Internal Revenue Service (IRS): federal agency responsible for the collection of federal taxes, including personal and corporate, Social Security, and excise and gift taxes.

International Stock Mutual Fund: mutual fund that contains international or overseas companies.

Investment: account or arrangement in which one would put their money for long-term growth; should not be withdrawn for a suggested minimum of five years.

Large-Cap Fund: funds comprised of large, well-established companies.

Liability Insurance: policy that protects an individual in the event of a lawsuit due to injury on one's personal property or as the result of an automobile accident.

Life Insurance: type of insurance designed to replace income lost due to death; traditionally two types: term and cash value.

Liquidity: quality of an asset that permits it to be converted quickly into cash without loss of value; availability of money; as there is more liquidity, there is typically less return.

Load Fund: mutual fund that sells shares with a sales charge of typically 2-6% of the net amount indicated; some no-load funds also levy distribution fees permitted by Article 12b-1 of the Investment Company Act; these are typically 0.25%; a true no-load fund has no sales charge.

Loan To Value (LTV): value of a property versus the amount borrowed against it; Example: a 70/30 LTV means that the property owner owes 70% of the item's worth and owns 30% of the item's worth.

Long-Term Care Insurance: policy that covers the cost of nursing home or in-home care insurance; recommended for everyone over age 60.

Low-Load Fund: mutual fund that charges a sales commission equal to 3% or less of the amount invested.

Medicare: federal government program of transfer payments for certain health care expenses for citizens 65 or older; managed by the Social Security Administration.

Mid-Cap Fund: mutual fund containing a group of medium-sized companies that are growing.

Money Market Fund: mutual fund that seeks to maintain a stable share price and to earn current income by investing in interest-bearing instruments with short-term (usually 90 days or less) maturities.

Mortgage: loan secured by the collateral of some specified real estate property, which obligates the borrower to make a predetermined series of payments.

Mortgage Life Insurance: insurance policy that pays off the remaining balance of the insured person's mortgage at death.

Multiple Listings Service (MLS): computer program used by realtors to search frequently updated listings of available properties in order to find prospective homes for their clients.

Mutual Fund: pool of money managed by an investment company and invested in multiple companies, bonds, etc.; offers investors a variety of goals, depending on the fund and its investment charter; often used to generate income on a regular basis or to preserve an investor's money; sometimes used to invest in companies that are growing at a rapid pace.

Nest Egg: sum of money earmarked for ongoing living expenses at retirement or when employment income otherwise stops.

No-Load Mutual Fund: open-ended investment company whose shares are sold without a sales charge; might include other distribution charges, such as Article 12b-1 fees, but a true no-load fund has neither a sales charge nor a distribution fee.

Not for Profit also called Non-Profit Organization: An incorporated organization, as defined within each state, which exists for educational or charitable purposes. Shareholders, Trustees, Directors do not benefit financially from the organization. A 501(c)(3) is an example of a non-profit organization.

Occupational Disability: type of insurance that provides an income in case the insured becomes unable to perform the job he/she was educated or trained to do.

Owner Financing: type of home loan in which the existing owner acts as the mortgage holder; payments are made to the owner, rather than to a mortgage company or bank.

Payroll Deduction: amount subtracted from a paycheck, either by government requirement (mandatory taxes, Social Security, etc.) or at the employee's request (health insurance, retirement plan, etc.).

Preauthorized Checking (PAC): system of automatic payment processing by which bills, deposits, and payments are handled electronically and at regular intervals or on a predetermined schedule.

Premium: amount you pay monthly, quarterly, semi-annually, or annually to purchase different types of insurance.

Principal: original amount of money invested, excluding any interest or dividends; also called the face value of a loan, excluding interest.

Private Mortgage Insurance (PMI): policy paid by the mortgage borrower that protects the lender against loss resulting from default on a mortgage loan.

Pro Rata: debt repayment plan by which the borrower repays each lender a fair percentage of the total debt owed when one cannot make the minimum payments on a debt.

Prospectus: official document that contains information required by the Securities and Exchange Commission to describe a mutual fund.

Rate of Return: return on an investment expressed as a percentage of its cost; also called yield.

Renter's Insurance: see Contents Insurance.

Replacement Cost: insurance that pays the actual cost of replacing your home and its contents after a catastrophic event.

Risk: degree of uncertainty of return on an asset; in business, the likelihood of loss or reduced profit.

Risk Return Ratio: relationship of substantial reward in comparison to the amount of risk taken.

Rollover: movement of funds from a tax-deferred retirement plan from one qualified plan or custodian to another; incurs no immediate tax liabilities or penalties, but requires IRS reporting.

Roth IRA: retirement account funded with after-tax dollars that subsequently grows tax free.

Roth 401(k): employer-sponsored retirement savings account that is funded with after-tax dollars and subsequently grows tax free.

Rule of 72: way of quickly determining a rough estimate for how long it will take to double an investment at a given rate of return; found by dividing 72 by the rate of return.

Rule of 78: pre-payment penalty in a financing contract; the portion of a 90-days-same-as-cash agreement that states that the entire loan amount plus the interest accumulated over the first 90 days becomes due immediately.

Savings Bond: certificate representing a debt; Example: U.S. savings bond is a loan to the government in which the government agrees to repay the amount borrowed, with interest, to the bondholder; government bonds are issued in face value denominations from $50 to $10,000 with local and state tax-free interest and semi-annually adjusted interest rates.

Self-Insured: condition of wealth at which time one no longer needs an outside insurance policy to cover a loss.

Share: piece of ownership in a company stock or mutual fund.

Short-Term Disability: minimal period of incapacitation; often used to describe an insurance policy that insures one's income for the immediate future following an incapacitating event.

Simple Interest: interest credited daily, monthly, quarterly, semi-annually, or annually on principal only, not previously credited interest.

Simple IRA: salary deduction plan for retirement benefits provided by some small companies with fewer than 100 employees.

Simplified Employee Pension Plan (SEP): pension plan in which both the employee and the employer contribute to an individual retirement account; also available to the self-employed.

Small-Cap Fund: mutual fund that invests in companies whose market value is less than $1 billion; largely consists of smaller, more volatile companies; also called aggressive growth stock mutual fund.

Social Security: federal government program of transfer payments for retirement, disability, or the loss of income from a parent or guardian; funds come from a tax on income, which is a payroll deduction labeled FICA.

Stocks: securities that represent part ownership or equity in a corporation, wherein each share is a claim on its proportionate stake in the corporation's assets and profits, some of which may be paid out as dividends.

Stop-Loss: total out-of-pocket expense for health insurance; once reached, insurance will pay 100%.

Tax Deduction: expense that a taxpayer is allowed to deduct from taxable income; examples include money paid as home mortgage interest and charitable donations.

Tax-Deferred Income: dividends, interest, and unrealized capital gains on investments in a qualified account, such as a retirement plan, in which income is not subject to taxation until a withdrawal is made.

Tax Exemptions: amount that a taxpayer who meets certain criteria can subtract from a taxable income; see tax credit and tax deduction.

Term Insurance: life insurance coverage for a specified period of time.

Title Insurance: coverage that protects a policyholder from future challenges to the title claim of a property that may result in loss of the property.

Umbrella Liability Insurance: insurance policy that acts as a protective covering over your home and car against liability caused by an accident.

Uniform Gifts to Minors Act (UGMA): legislation that provides a tax-effective manner of transferring property to minors without the complications of trusts or guardianship restrictions.

Uniform Transfers to Minors Act (UTMA): law similar to the Uniform Gifts to Minors Act (UGMA) that extends the definition of gifts to include real estate, paintings, royalties, and patents.

Universal Life: type of life insurance policy, similar to cash value but with better projected returns.

VA Loan: type of mortgage loan designed to benefit veterans that allows for a true zero-down mortgage; generally more expensive than a conventional mortgage.

Value Fund: mutual fund that emphasizes stocks of companies whose growth prospects are generally regarded as sub-par by the market, resulting in value stocks typically priced below average in comparison with such factors as revenue, earnings, book value, and dividends.

Variable Annuity: annuity that has a varying rate of return based on the mutual funds in which one has invested; also see annuity.

Variable Life: type of life insurance that is similar to cash value, but buys into mutual funds to project better returns.

Viatical: contractual arrangement in which a business buys life insurance policies from terminally ill patients for a percentage of the face value.

Volatility: fluctuations in market value of a mutual fund or other security; the greater a fund's volatility, the wider the fluctuations between high and low prices.

Whole Life Insurance: type of insurance that contains a low-yield savings plan within the insurance policy; more expensive than term insurance.

Zero-Based Budget: cash flow plan that assigns an expense to every dollar of one's income, wherein the total income minus the total expenses equals zero.

FORMS

THE BASIC QUICKIE BUDGET INSTRUCTIONS

This form will help you get your feet wet in the area of budgeting. It is only one page and should not be intimidating as you get started. The purpose of this form is to show you exactly how much money you need every month in order to survive. We won't get into the details of your credit card bills, student loans and other consumer debts here. This is just to give you a starting point as you begin to take control of your money.

There are four columns on this form:

1 *Monthly Total*
- This column shows you how much you are spending on necessities each month.
- If you do not know the amount, write down your best estimate.
- If an estimate is grossly inaccurate, then you may have never even noticed how much you were spending in that area before now. Don't beat yourself up about this!

2 *Payoff Total*
- Write down how much money is required to completely pay off that item.
- This line only appears in the relevant categories (mortgage, car debt, etc.).

3 *How Far Behind?*
- If your account is past due in any category, write down how many days you are behind.
- If you are up-to-date, simply write a zero or "N/A" (not applicable) in this column.

4 *Type of Account*
- Write in how this area is paid—by check, automatic bank draft, cash, etc.
- Early in the program, you will see the benefits of using cash for certain items. Challenge yourself by identifying categories for which you can use cash only.
- The asterisks (*) on the form indicate areas in which a cash-based approach could be helpful.

THE BASIC QUICKIE BUDGET

Item	[1] Monthly Total	[2] Payoff Total	[3] How Far Behind	[4] Type of Account
GIVING	_____		_____	_____
SAVING	_____		_____	_____
HOUSING				
First Mortgage	_____	_____	_____	_____
Second Mortgage	_____	_____	_____	_____
Repairs/Mn. Fee	_____		_____	_____
UTILITIES				
Electricity	_____		_____	_____
Water	_____		_____	_____
Gas	_____		_____	_____
Phone	_____		_____	_____
Trash	_____		_____	_____
Cable	_____		_____	_____
*Food	_____		_____	_____
TRANSPORTATION				
Car Payment	_____	_____	_____	_____
Car Payment	_____	_____	_____	_____
*Gas & Oil	_____		_____	_____
*Repairs & Tires	_____		_____	_____
Car Insurance	_____		_____	_____
*CLOTHING	_____		_____	_____
PERSONAL				
Disability Ins.	_____		_____	_____
Health Insurance	_____		_____	_____
Life Insurance	_____		_____	_____
Child Care	_____		_____	_____
*Entertainment	_____		_____	_____
OTHER MISC.	_____		_____	_____

TOTAL MONTHLY NECESSITIES _____

01 MAJOR COMPONENTS OF A HEALTHY FINANCIAL PLAN

	Action Needed	*Action Date*
Written Cash Flow Plan	_____	_____
Will and/or Estate Plan	_____	_____
Debt Reduction Plan	_____	_____
Tax Reduction Plan	_____	_____
Emergency Funding	_____	_____
Retirement Funding	_____	_____
College Funding	_____	_____
Charitable Giving	_____	_____
Teach My Children	_____	_____
Life Insurance	_____	_____
Health Insurance	_____	_____
Disability Insurance	_____	_____
Auto Insurance	_____	_____
Homeowner's Insurance	_____	_____

I (We) _____, (a) responsible adult(s), do hereby promise to take the above stated actions by the above stated dates to financially secure the well-being of my (our) family and myself (ourselves).

Signed:_____ Date:_____

Signed:_____ Date:_____

02 | CONSUMER EQUITY SHEET

Item / Describe	Value	–	Debt	=	Equity
Real Estate _____	_____		_____		_____
Real Estate _____	_____		_____		_____
Car _____	_____		_____		_____
Car _____	_____		_____		_____
Cash On Hand	_____		_____		_____
Checking Account	_____		_____		_____
Checking Account	_____		_____		_____
Savings Account	_____		_____		_____
Money Market Account	_____		_____		_____
Mutual Funds	_____		_____		_____
Retirement Plan 1	_____		_____		_____
Retirement Plan 2	_____		_____		_____
Cash Value (Insurance)	_____		_____		_____
Household Items	_____		_____		_____
Jewelry	_____		_____		_____
Antiques	_____		_____		_____
Boat	_____		_____		_____
Unsecured Debt (Negative)	_____		_____		_____
Credit Card Debt (Negative)	_____		_____		_____
Other _____	_____		_____		_____
Other _____	_____		_____		_____
Other _____	_____		_____		_____
TOTAL	_____		_____		_____

03 INCOME SOURCES

Source	Amount	Period/Describe
Salary 1	_____	_____
Salary 2	_____	_____
Salary 3	_____	_____
Bonus	_____	_____
Self-Employment	_____	_____
Interest Income	_____	_____
Dividend Income	_____	_____
Royalty Income	_____	_____
Rents	_____	_____
Notes	_____	_____
Alimony	_____	_____
Child Support	_____	_____
AFDC	_____	_____
Unemployment	_____	_____
Social Security	_____	_____
Pension	_____	_____
Annuity	_____	_____
Disability Income	_____	_____
Cash Gifts	_____	_____
Trust Fund	_____	_____
Other_____	_____	_____
Other_____	_____	_____
Other_____	_____	_____
TOTAL	_____	

Payments you make on a non-monthly basis, such as insurance premiums and taxes, can be budget busters if you do not plan for them every month. Therefore, you must annualize the cost and convert these to monthly budget items. That way, you can save the money each month and will not be caught off-guard when your bi-monthly, quarterly, semi-annual or annual bills come due. Simply divide the annual cost by 12 to determine the monthly amount you should save for each item.

Item Needed	Annual Amount		Monthly Amount
Real Estate Taxes	_____	/ 12 =	_____
Homeowner's Insurance	_____	/ 12 =	_____
Home Repairs	_____	/ 12 =	_____
Replace Furniture	_____	/ 12 =	_____
Medical Bills	_____	/ 12 =	_____
Health Insurance	_____	/ 12 =	_____
Life Insurance	_____	/ 12 =	_____
Disability Insurance	_____	/ 12 =	_____
Car Insurance	_____	/ 12 =	_____
Car Repair/Tags	_____	/ 12 =	_____
Replace Car	_____	/ 12 =	_____
Clothing	_____	/ 12 =	_____
Tuition	_____	/ 12 =	_____
Bank Note	_____	/ 12 =	_____
IRS (Self-Employed)	_____	/ 12 =	_____
Vacation	_____	/ 12 =	_____
Gifts (including Christmas)	_____	/ 12 =	_____
Other: _____	_____	/ 12 =	_____

Every single dollar of your income should be allocated to some category on this form. When you're done, your total income minus expenses should equal zero. If it doesn't, then you need to adjust some categories (such as debt reduction, giving or saving) so that it does equal zero. Use some common sense here, too. Do not leave things like clothes, car repairs or home improvements off this list. If you don't plan for these things, you're only setting yourself up for failure later.

Yes, this budget form is long. It's really long. We do that so that we can list practically every expense imaginable on this form to prevent you from forgetting something. Don't expect to put something on every line item. Just use the ones that are relevant to your specific situation.

Every main category on this form has subcategories. Fill in the monthly expense for each subcategory, and then write down the grand total for that category. Later, as you actually pay the bills and work through the month, use the "Actually Spent" column to record what you really spent in each area. If there is a substantial difference between what you budgeted and what you spent, then you'll need to readjust the budget to make up for the difference. If one category continually comes up over or short for two or three months, you'll need to adjust the budgeted amount accordingly.

Notes:

- An asterisk (*) beside an item indicates an area for which you should use a cash envelope system.

- The emergency fund should get all the savings until you've completed your full emergency fund of three to six months of expenses (Baby Step 3).

- Don't forget to include your annualized items from the "Lump Sum Payment Planning" sheet (Form 4), including your Christmas gift planning.

05 | MONTHLY CASH FLOW PLAN

Budgeted Item	Sub Total	TOTAL	Actually Spent	% of Take Home Pay
CHARITABLE GIFTS		_____	_____	_____
SAVING				
Emergency Fund	_____		_____	
Retirement Fund	_____		_____	
College Fund	_____	_____	_____	_____
HOUSING				
First Mortgage	_____		_____	
Second Mortgage	_____		_____	
Real Estate Taxes	_____		_____	
Homeowner's Ins.	_____		_____	
Repairs or Mn. Fee	_____		_____	
Replace Furniture	_____		_____	
Other _____	_____	_____	_____	_____
UTILITIES				
Electricity	_____		_____	
Water	_____		_____	
Gas	_____		_____	
Phone	_____		_____	
Trash	_____		_____	
Cable	_____	_____	_____	_____
*FOOD				
*Grocery	_____		_____	
*Restaurants	_____	_____	_____	_____
TRANSPORTATION				
Car Payment	_____		_____	
Car Payment	_____		_____	
*Gas and Oil	_____		_____	
*Repairs and Tires	_____		_____	
Car Insurance	_____		_____	
License and Taxes	_____		_____	
Car Replacement	_____	_____	_____	_____
PAGE 1 TOTAL		_____	_____	

Budgeted Item	Sub Total	TOTAL	Actually Spent	% of Take Home Pay
*CLOTHING				
*Children	_____		_____	
*Adults	_____		_____	
*Cleaning/Laundry	_____	_____	_____	_____
MEDICAL/HEALTH				
Disability Insurance	_____		_____	
Health Insurance	_____		_____	
Doctor Bills	_____		_____	
Dentist	_____		_____	
Optometrist	_____		_____	
Medications	_____	_____	_____	_____
PERSONAL				
Life Insurance	_____		_____	
Child Care	_____		_____	
*Baby Sitter	_____		_____	
*Toiletries	_____		_____	
*Cosmetics	_____		_____	
*Hair Care	_____		_____	
Education/Adult	_____		_____	
School Tuition	_____		_____	
School Supplies	_____		_____	
Child Support	_____		_____	
Alimony	_____		_____	
Subscriptions	_____		_____	
Organization Dues	_____		_____	
Gifts (incl. Christmas)	_____		_____	
Miscellaneous	_____		_____	
*Blow Money	_____	_____	_____	_____

PAGE 2 TOTAL   _____

Budgeted Item	Sub Total	TOTAL	Actually Spent	% of Take Home Pay
RECREATION				
*Entertainment	_____		_____	
Vacation	_____	_____	_____	_____
DEBTS (Hopefully -0-)				
Visa 1	_____		_____	
Visa 2	_____		_____	
Master Card 1	_____		_____	
Master Card 2	_____		_____	
American Express	_____		_____	
Discover Card	_____		_____	
Gas Card 1	_____		_____	
Gas Card 2	_____		_____	
Dept. Store Card 1	_____		_____	
Dept. Store Card 2	_____		_____	
Finance Co. 1	_____		_____	
Finance Co. 2	_____		_____	
Credit Line	_____		_____	
Student Loan 1	_____		_____	
Student Loan 2	_____		_____	
Other _____	_____		_____	
Other _____	_____		_____	
Other _____	_____		_____	
Other _____	_____	_____	_____	_____
PAGE 3 TOTAL		_____	_____	
PAGE 2 TOTAL		_____	_____	
PAGE 1 TOTAL		_____	_____	
GRAND TOTAL		_____	_____	
TOTAL HOUSEHOLD INCOME		_____		
		ZERO		

06 | RECOMMENDED PERCENTAGES

How much of your income should be spent on housing, giving, food, etc.? Through experience and research, we recommend the following percentages. However, you should remember that these are only *recommended* percentages. If you have an unusually high or low income, then these numbers could change dramatically. For example, if you have a high income, the percentage that is spent on food will be much lower than someone who earns half of that.

If you find that you spend much more in one category than we recommend, however, it may be necessary to adjust your lifestyle in that area in order to enjoy more freedom and flexibility across the board.

Item	Actual %	Recommended %
CHARITABLE GIFTS	_____	10–15%
SAVING	_____	5–10%
HOUSING	_____	25–35%
UTILITIES	_____	5–10%
FOOD	_____	5–15%
TRANSPORTATION	_____	10–15%
CLOTHING	_____	2–7%
MEDICAL/HEALTH	_____	5–10%
PERSONAL	_____	5–10%
RECREATION	_____	5–10%
DEBTS	_____	5–10%

This form goes into deeper detail than the "Monthly Cash Flow Plan" (Form 5). Here, you will allocate—or spend—all of your money from each individual pay period.

There are four columns on this form, representing the four weeks in a given month. You will use one column for each week you get paid. If you are married and your spouse earns an income, you will both use this same form. For weeks in which you both receive a paycheck, add those two incomes together and use a single column.

Now, go down the list and allocate each expense to a specific payday, using your bills' due dates as a guide. For example, if your phone bill is due on the 22nd and you get paid on the 15th and 30th, then you know that you would probably pay that bill from your income on the 15th. The point is to anticipate your upcoming expenses and income and plan accordingly.

Beside each line item, you'll see two blanks separated by a slash (/). Put the expense to the left of the slash and the remaining income from that pay period to the right of the slash. As you work your way down the column, the income remaining should diminish until you reach a perfect zero at the bottom of the list. If you have money left over at the end of the column, go back and adjust an area, such as savings or giving, so that you spend every single dollar.

NOTES:
1. If you have an irregular income, such as self-employment or commissions, you should use the "Irregular Income Planning" sheet (Form 8) instead of this "Allocated Spending Plan."

2. If you know that you have an impulse spending problem, you may want to allocate more money to the "Blow" category. That way, you are at least setting up some spending boundaries.

3. An asterisk (*) beside an item indicates an area for which you should use a cash envelope system.

07 | ALLOCATED SPENDING PLAN

PAY PERIOD: ____ / ____   ____ / ____   ____ / ____   ____ / ____

ITEM:
INCOME   _____   _____   _____   _____

CHARITABLE   ____ / ____   ____ / ____   ____ / ____   ____ / ____

SAVING

Emergency Fund   ____ / ____   ____ / ____   ____ / ____   ____ / ____
Retirement Fund   ____ / ____   ____ / ____   ____ / ____   ____ / ____
College Fund   ____ / ____   ____ / ____   ____ / ____   ____ / ____

HOUSING

First Mortgage   ____ / ____   ____ / ____   ____ / ____   ____ / ____
Second Mortgage   ____ / ____   ____ / ____   ____ / ____   ____ / ____
Real Estate Taxes   ____ / ____   ____ / ____   ____ / ____   ____ / ____
Homeowner's Ins.   ____ / ____   ____ / ____   ____ / ____   ____ / ____
Repairs or Mn. Fees   ____ / ____   ____ / ____   ____ / ____   ____ / ____
Replace Furniture   ____ / ____   ____ / ____   ____ / ____   ____ / ____
Other ____   ____ / ____   ____ / ____   ____ / ____   ____ / ____

UTILITIES

Electricity   ____ / ____   ____ / ____   ____ / ____   ____ / ____
Water   ____ / ____   ____ / ____   ____ / ____   ____ / ____
Gas   ____ / ____   ____ / ____   ____ / ____   ____ / ____
Phone   ____ / ____   ____ / ____   ____ / ____   ____ / ____
Trash   ____ / ____   ____ / ____   ____ / ____   ____ / ____
Cable   ____ / ____   ____ / ____   ____ / ____   ____ / ____

*FOOD

*Grocery   ____ / ____   ____ / ____   ____ / ____   ____ / ____
*Restaurants   ____ / ____   ____ / ____   ____ / ____   ____ / ____

TRANSPORTATION

Car Payment _____ / _____ _____ / _____ _____ / _____ _____ / _____

Car Payment _____ / _____ _____ / _____ _____ / _____ _____ / _____

* Gas and Oil _____ / _____ _____ / _____ _____ / _____ _____ / _____

* Repairs and Tires _____ / _____ _____ / _____ _____ / _____ _____ / _____

Car Insurance _____ / _____ _____ / _____ _____ / _____ _____ / _____

License and Taxes _____ / _____ _____ / _____ _____ / _____ _____ / _____

Car Replacement _____ / _____ _____ / _____ _____ / _____ _____ / _____

*CLOTHING

* Children _____ / _____ _____ / _____ _____ / _____ _____ / _____

* Adults _____ / _____ _____ / _____ _____ / _____ _____ / _____

* Cleaning/Laundry _____ / _____ _____ / _____ _____ / _____ _____ / _____

MEDICAL/HEALTH

Disability Insurance _____ / _____ _____ / _____ _____ / _____ _____ / _____

Health Insurance _____ / _____ _____ / _____ _____ / _____ _____ / _____

Doctor _____ / _____ _____ / _____ _____ / _____ _____ / _____

Dentist _____ / _____ _____ / _____ _____ / _____ _____ / _____

Optometrist _____ / _____ _____ / _____ _____ / _____ _____ / _____

Medications _____ / _____ _____ / _____ _____ / _____ _____ / _____

PERSONAL

Life Insurance _____ / _____ _____ / _____ _____ / _____ _____ / _____

Child Care _____ / _____ _____ / _____ _____ / _____ _____ / _____

* Baby Sitter _____ / _____ _____ / _____ _____ / _____ _____ / _____

* Toiletries _____ / _____ _____ / _____ _____ / _____ _____ / _____

* Cosmetics _____ / _____ _____ / _____ _____ / _____ _____ / _____

* Hair Care _____ / _____ _____ / _____ _____ / _____ _____ / _____

Education/Adult _____ / _____ _____ / _____ _____ / _____ _____ / _____

School Tuition _____ / _____ _____ / _____ _____ / _____ _____ / _____

School Supplies _____ / _____ _____ / _____ _____ / _____ _____ / _____

Child Support _____ / _____ _____ / _____ _____ / _____ _____ / _____

Alimony _____ /_____ _____ /_____ _____ /_____ _____ /_____

Subscriptions _____ /_____ _____ /_____ _____ /_____ _____ /_____

Organization Dues _____ /_____ _____ /_____ _____ /_____ _____ /_____

Gifts (incl. Christmas) _____ /_____ _____ /_____ _____ /_____ _____ /_____

Miscellaneous _____ /_____ _____ /_____ _____ /_____ _____ /_____

*BLOW $$ _____ /_____ _____ /_____ _____ /_____ _____ /_____

RECREATION

* Entertainment _____ /_____ _____ /_____ _____ /_____ _____ /_____

Vacation _____ /_____ _____ /_____ _____ /_____ _____ /_____

DEBTS (Hopefully -0-)

Visa 1 _____ /_____ _____ /_____ _____ /_____ _____ /_____

Visa 2 _____ /_____ _____ /_____ _____ /_____ _____ /_____

MasterCard 1 _____ /_____ _____ /_____ _____ /_____ _____ /_____

MasterCard 2 _____ /_____ _____ /_____ _____ /_____ _____ /_____

American Express _____ /_____ _____ /_____ _____ /_____ _____ /_____

Discover Card _____ /_____ _____ /_____ _____ /_____ _____ /_____

Gas Card 1 _____ /_____ _____ /_____ _____ /_____ _____ /_____

Gas Card 2 _____ /_____ _____ /_____ _____ /_____ _____ /_____

Dept. Store Card 1 _____ /_____ _____ /_____ _____ /_____ _____ /_____

Dept. Store Card 2 _____ /_____ _____ /_____ _____ /_____ _____ /_____

Finance Co. 1 _____ /_____ _____ /_____ _____ /_____ _____ /_____

Finance Co. 2 _____ /_____ _____ /_____ _____ /_____ _____ /_____

Credit Line _____ /_____ _____ /_____ _____ /_____ _____ /_____

Student Loan 1 _____ /_____ _____ /_____ _____ /_____ _____ /_____

Student Loan 2 _____ /_____ _____ /_____ _____ /_____ _____ /_____

Other _____ _____ /_____ _____ /_____ _____ /_____ _____ /_____

Other _____ _____ /_____ _____ /_____ _____ /_____ _____ /_____

08 | IRREGULAR INCOME PLANNING

Many people have an "irregular" income, which simply means that their compensation fluctuates from month to month. This is especially common for the self-employed, as well as commission-based salespeople. While this makes it more difficult to predict your income, you are still responsible for doing a monthly budget!

The "Monthly Cash Flow Plan" (Form 5) should remain a crucial part of your plan, as it lays out exactly how much money you need to bring home each month to survive and prosper. However, instead of doing the "Allocated Spending Plan" (Form 7), you will use this "Irregular Income Planning" sheet.

On this form, simply look at the individual items from your "Monthly Cash Flow Plan" sheet and prioritize them by importance. Ask yourself, "If I only have enough money to pay one thing, what would that be?" Put that at the top of your list. Then, ask yourself, "If I only have enough money to pay one more thing, what would that be?" That's number two. Keep this up all the way down the list.

With your list in place, you're ready to get paid. If you get a $1,500 paycheck, you will spend that $1,500 right down the list until it is gone, recording the cumulative amount spent in the "Cumulative Amount" column. At that point, you're finished spending, no matter what remains unpaid on the list. That's why the most important things are at the top of the list, right?

Be prepared to stand your ground. Things usually have a way of seeming important when they are only urgent. For example, a once-in-a-lifetime opportunity to see your favorite band perform live may seem important, but in reality, it is only urgent, meaning that it is time-sensitive. Urgency alone should not move an item to the top of this list!

Item	Amount	Cumulative Amount

09 BREAKDOWN OF SAVINGS

After you have fully funded your emergency fund, you can start to save for other items, such as furniture, car replacement, home maintenance or a vacation. This sheet will remind you that every dollar in your savings account is already committed to something. For example, it's a bad idea to take money away from car repairs to pay for an impulse Hawaiian vacation, even if you pay cash for it. What would you do if the car broke down the week you got back home? However, it can be okay to re-assign the dollars to another category, as long as you do it on purpose and it doesn't put you in a pinch in another category. Keep up with your breakdown of savings every month, one quarter at a time.

Item	Balance By Month		
	_____	_____	_____
Emergency Fund (1) $1,000	_____	_____	_____
Emergency Fund (2) 3-6 months	_____	_____	_____
Retirement Fund	_____	_____	_____
College Fund	_____	_____	_____
Real Estate Taxes	_____	_____	_____
Homeowner's Insurance	_____	_____	_____
Repairs or Mn. Fee	_____	_____	_____
Replace Furniture	_____	_____	_____
Car Insurance	_____	_____	_____
Car Replacement	_____	_____	_____
Disability Insurance	_____	_____	_____
Health Insurance	_____	_____	_____
Doctor	_____	_____	_____
Dentist	_____	_____	_____
Optometrist	_____	_____	_____
Life Insurance	_____	_____	_____
School Tuition	_____	_____	_____
School Supplies	_____	_____	_____
Gifts (incl. Christmas)	_____	_____	_____
Vacation	_____	_____	_____
Other _____	_____	_____	_____
Other _____	_____	_____	_____
TOTAL	_____	_____	_____

10 | DEBT SNOWBALL

Now it's time to knock out that debt! List your debts in order, from the smallest balance to the largest. Don't be concerned with interest rates, unless two debts have a similar payoff balance. In that case, list the one with the higher interest rate first. As you start eliminating debts, you'll start to build some serious momentum. These quick wins will keep you motivated, so you'll be able to stay on track.

The idea of the snowball is simple: pay minimum payments on all of your debts except for the smallest one. Then, attack that one with gazelle intensity! Every extra dollar you can get your hands on should be thrown at that smallest debt until it is gone. Then, you attack the second one. Every time you pay a debt off, you add its old minimum payment to your next debt payments.

So, as the snowball rolls over, it picks up more snow. Get it?

Redo this sheet every time you pay off a debt so that you can see how close you're getting to total debt freedom. Keep the old sheets for encouragement—or to wallpaper the bathroom in your debt-free house someday!

The "New Payment" is the total of the previous debt's payment PLUS the current debt's minimum. As these payments compound, you'll start making huge payments as you work down the list until you can eventually call Dave's radio show and scream, "I'M DEBT FREE!"

10 DEBT SNOWBALL

Item	Total Payoff	Minimum Payment	New Payment
_____	_____	_____	_____
_____	_____	_____	_____
_____	_____	_____	_____
_____	_____	_____	_____
_____	_____	_____	_____
_____	_____	_____	_____
_____	_____	_____	_____
_____	_____	_____	_____
_____	_____	_____	_____
_____	_____	_____	_____
_____	_____	_____	_____
_____	_____	_____	_____
_____	_____	_____	_____
_____	_____	_____	_____
_____	_____	_____	_____
_____	_____	_____	_____
_____	_____	_____	_____
_____	_____	_____	_____
_____	_____	_____	_____

"Pro rata" means the fair share, or the percent of your total debt each creditor represents. This will determine how much you should send them when you cannot make the minimum payments. Even if you cannot pay your creditors what they request, you should pay everyone as much as you can. Send the check for their pro rata share, along with a copy of your budget and this form, every month. Do this even if the creditor says they will not accept it.

Do you need to use the pro rata plan?

First, use your monthly cash flow plan to determine your total disposable income. Simply write down your income on the line at the top of the form. Then, write down the total you spend on necessities (not including consumer debt) each month. Subtract the necessity expense from the income, and you are left with your disposable income. This is the money you have to put toward your debts.

Second, add up your total amount of debt, not including your home, and write that in the blank provided. Below that, write in the total of the minimum monthly payments on all your debts. If the total of your minimum payments is greater than your total disposable income, you need to use the pro rata plan.

How to Use This Form

This form has six columns:
1. Item: the name and type of the account.
2. Total Payoff: the total amount due on the account.
3. Total Debt: the combined total of all your debts.
4. Percent: the portion of the total debt load that each account represents. You can calculate this by simply dividing the Total Payoff by the Total Debt for each line.
5. Disposable Income: the amount of money you have left after paying necessities.
6. New Payment: the amount that you will now send to each creditor. Simply multiply the numbers in each line's Percent and Disposable Income columns for this figure.

The pro rata plan helps you to meet your obligations to the best of your ability. Your creditors will not like receiving less than their required minimum payments. However, if you keep sending them checks, they'll most likely keep cashing them.

11 | PRO RATA DEBT LIST

Income _____

Necessity Expense – _____

Disposable Income = _____

Total Debt: _____

Total Minimum Payments: _____

Item	Total Payoff	Total Debt	Percent	Disposable Income	New Payment
_____	_____ / _____	= _____	X _____	= _____
_____	_____ / _____	= _____	X _____	= _____
_____	_____ / _____	= _____	X _____	= _____
_____	_____ / _____	= _____	X _____	= _____
_____	_____ / _____	= _____	X _____	= _____
_____	_____ / _____	= _____	X _____	= _____
_____	_____ / _____	= _____	X _____	= _____
_____	_____ / _____	= _____	X _____	= _____
_____	_____ / _____	= _____	X _____	= _____
_____	_____ / _____	= _____	X _____	= _____
_____	_____ / _____	= _____	X _____	= _____
_____	_____ / _____	= _____	X _____	= _____
_____	_____ / _____	= _____	X _____	= _____
_____	_____ / _____	= _____	X _____	= _____
_____	_____ / _____	= _____	X _____	= _____
_____	_____ / _____	= _____	X _____	= _____
_____	_____ / _____	= _____	X _____	= _____
_____	_____ / _____	= _____	X _____	= _____
_____	_____ / _____	= _____	X _____	= _____
_____	_____ / _____	= _____	X _____	= _____

Too many people use the READY-FIRE-AIM approach to retirement planning. That's a bad plan. You need to aim first. Your assignment is to determine how much per month you should be saving at 12% interest in order to retire at 65 with the amount you need.

If you save at 12% and inflation is at 4%, then you are moving ahead of inflation at a net of 8% per year. If you invest your nest egg at retirement at 12% and want to break even with 4% inflation, you will be living on 8% income.

Step 1:   Annual income (today) you wish to retire on: _____

Divide by .08

(Nest egg needed)equals: _____

Step 2:   To achieve that nest egg you will save at 12%, netting 8% after inflation. So, we will target that nest egg using 8%.

Nest Egg Needed $ _____

Multiply by Factor   X _____

Monthly Savings Needed   = _____

Note: Be sure to try one or two examples if you wait 5 or 10 years to start.

8% FACTORS (SELECT THE ONE THAT MATCHES YOUR AGE)

Your Age	Years to Save	Factor	Your Age	Years to Save	Factor
25	40	.000286	45	20	.001698
30	35	.000436	50	15	.002890
35	30	.000671	55	10	.005466
40	25	.001051	60	5	.013610

In order to have enough for college, you must aim at something. Your assignment is to determine how much per month you should be saving at 12% interest in order to have enough for college.

If you save at 12% and inflation is at 4%, then you are moving ahead of inflation at a net of 8% per year.

Step 1: In today's dollars, the annual cost of the college of your choice is:

Amount per year $ _____

X 4 years = $ _____

(hint: $15,000 to $25,000 annually)

Step 2: To achieve that college nest egg, you will save at 12%, netting 8% after inflation. So, we will target that nest egg using 8%.

Nest Egg Needed $ _____

Multiply by Factor X _____

Monthly Savings Needed = _____

Note: Be sure to try one or two examples if you wait 5 or 10 years to start.

8% FACTORS (SELECT THE ONE THAT MATCHES YOUR CHILD'S AGE)

Child's Age	Years to Save	Factor	Child's Age	Years to Save	Factor
0	18	.002083	8	10	.005466
2	16	.002583	10	8	.007470
4	14	.003247	12	6	.010867
6	12	.004158	14	4	.017746

CARD NAME	NUMBER	ADDRESS	PHONE #	CLOSED	WRITTEN CONFIRMATION REQUESTED	WRITTEN CONFIRMATION RECEIVED
Visa	1234 561989 12	1234 Poplar Grove, suite 130	123-456-7890	09/21/06	09/21/06	11/21/06

CARD NAME	NUMBER	ADDRESS	PHONE #	CLOSED		WRITTEN CONFIRMATION REQUESTED	WRITTEN CONFIRMATION RECEIVED
Visa	1234 561989 12	1234 Poplar Grove, suite 130	123-456-1890	09/21/06		09/21/06	11/21/06

TYPE	COMPANY	PLAN ID #	POLICY #	AMOUNT	AGENT	PHONE #
Term life	ABC Inurance	1234 561989 12	1234 561989 12	$150,000	John Smith	456-7890

MORTGAGE INFORMATION

TYPE	COMPANY	PLAN ID #	POLICY #	AMOUNT	AGENT	PHONE #

15 INSURANCE COVERAGE RECAP

TYPE	COMPANY	PLAN ID #	POLICY #	AMOUNT	AGENT	PHONE #
Term life	ABC Inurance	1234 561989 12	1234 561989 12	$450,000	John Smith	456-1890

MORTGAGE INFORMATION

TYPE	COMPANY	PLAN ID #	POLICY #	AMOUNT	AGENT	PHONE #

HOW TO FIGURE YOUR NEW PAYMENT

Use this worksheet to estimate the monthly mortgage payment on a 15-year loan compared to a 30-year loan.

_____ / 1,000 = _____ X _____ = _____
SALES PRICE   #1,000'S   FACTOR   MONTHLY PAYMENT

Example: Sales Price - $150,000, 15 years at 6%

$150,000 / 1,000 = _150_ X _8.44_ = _$1,266_
SALES PRICE   #1000'S   FACTOR   MONTHLY PAYMENT

MONTHLY PAYMENT PER $1,000 IN LOAN AMOUNT

Rate	15-Year	30-Year	Rate	15-Year	30-Year
4.5%	7.65	5.07	8.5%	9.85	7.69
5.0%	7.91	5.37	9.0%	10.15	8.05
5.5%	8.17	5.68	9.5%	10.44	8.41
6.0%	8.44	6.00	10.0%	10.75	8.78
6.5%	8.71	6.32	10.5%	11.05	9.15
7.0%	8.99	6.66	11.0%	11.37	9.52
7.5%	9.28	7.00	11.5%	11.68	9.90
8.0%	9.56	7.34	12.0%	12.00	10.29

SHOULD I REFINANCE?

This worksheet helps you decide whether or not it would make sense to refinance your current mortgage to a lower-interest loan.

_____ — _____ = _____

Current principal and
interest payment
(not including taxes & insurance)

New principal
and interest payment

Monthly savings

_____ / _____ = _____

Total closing costs

Monthly savings

Number of months
to break even

*Will you stay in your home longer than the number
of months to break even? If so, you are a candidate for a refinance.*

Example: Refinance on a $150,000 Mortgage at 8% to 6.5%

$1,434 current payment – $1,307 new payment = $127 savings

$2,300 closing cost divided by $127 savings = 18 months

ESTIMATED CLOSING COSTS TABLE

Loan Amount	Closing Costs	Loan Amount	Closing Costs	Loan Amount	Closing Costs
30,000	1,500	60,000	1,775	90,000	1,950
35,000	1,550	65,000	1,800	95,000	1,975
40,000	1,600	70,000	1,825	100,000	2,000
45,000	1,650	75,000	1,850	150,000	2,300
50,000	1,700	80,000	1,900	200,000	2,600
55,000	1,725	85,000	1,925	250,000	2,900

HOW TO FIGURE
THE CHANGE IN YOUR ARM

Your Adjustable Rate Mortgage (ARM) adjusts based on the movement of an index. You can find your index in your original note or mortgage. The most commonly used index is the Treasury Bill (T-Bill). The one-year ARM uses the one-year T-Bill, the three-year ARM uses the three-year T-Bill, and so on. Other commonly used indexes are the LIBOR and the 11th District Cost of Funds.

1. First, find out what index you use and when it is adjusted.

2. Next, find out (also from your loan paperwork) what margin was assigned to your loan (usually 2.59).

Basically, your ARM adjusts as the index moves.

The index is usually published daily in The Wall Street Journal.

So, if you have a one-year ARM that adjusts with the one-year T-Bill and a margin of 2.59 (which is typical), then, at the one-year anniversary of your closing, you would look up the one-year T-Bill in The Wall Street Journal. Add the T-Bill to your margin and you have your new rate (if it is not capped).

Example: T-Bill 4.41 plus margin 2.59 = 7% new interest rate.

Name of Index
Used by your ARM:_____   Index Adjustment   _____

Date that it is adjusted:_____   Margin   _____

New Interest Rate   _____

WARNING: *Almost all ARMs start belowmargin the first year, guaranteeing a payment increaseat anniversary unless rates DROP.*